SEX POSITIONS

*Sex Positions: The ultimate 3 in 1
Boxset/Bundle That Teaches You How Become
A Sex God & Make Your Lover Deeply
Addicted To You.*

JESSICA ANDERSON

TABLE OF CONTENTS

SEX POSITIONS

SEX POSITIONS FOR COUPLES

KAMA SUTRA

SEX POSITIONS

The Orgasm Bible

*Become a Sex God & Make Your
Lover Addicted To You*

JESSICA ANDERSON

INTRODUCTION

To our modern ears, the Kama Sutra has come to be synonymous with an exotic and enigmatic idea of sex. In the common media of television and movies, it is used as comic relief to represent something almost taboo, the full embodiment of the 'libido.' And while the Kama Sutra can definitely be regarded as a manual on lovemaking, more often than not we're only ever exposed to the most superficial elements of what is one of the more ancient and philosophically relevant Indian texts. Because while the Kama Sutra is explicit and descriptive in terms of describing the act of lovemaking and its nuances – both in a physical and emotional context – it is primarily a guide to *relationships*.

Love has always guided human affairs, and the Kama Sutra's main aim in ancient India was to maintain these bonds of love between women and men. It was their belief that the physical act of lovemaking – of sexual intercourse – was a holy endeavor and should be taken seriously. To explicate this idea that coitus was, in fact, a sacred act, it outlined a number of sexual positions ranging from foreplay to the actual act of penetration to post-coital embraces.

In the chapters that follow we will briefly consider the spiritual element that comprises the majority of the Kama Sutra, but will try to focus on some of the more physical aspects and how a proper fluency in some of the more unconventional sex positions can lead to a more fuller awareness of intimacy, a deeper emotional bond with your partner, and overall better experience of sex.

CHAPTER 1:
THE SPIRITUALITY OF LOVE

The problem with picking and choosing from an ancient text like the Kama Sutra, which is thought to have been compiled in the 2nd century (although it was likely composed somewhere between 400 and 300 BCE), is that for it to mean something you have to take it within the context of the time. In reality, only 20% of the actual Kama Sutra outlined explicit sexual positions and the majority of these that we will focus on were for heteronormative couples (although there are some queer-friendly passages in the text as well as suggestions). The Kama Sutra is compiled as a number of prove and poetic verses and is thought to be attributed to the sage Vatsyayana and most of the text takes into account Indian philosophy and how to live a virtuous life by elaborating on the nature of desire and its effect on our worldly persons.

For our purposes, it's important to analyze our own approach to relationships and love. How do we define love personally? As

something physical or intellectual, or both? This, really, is the purpose of the Kama Sutra: to make us think critically and emotionally about our interactions with those we hold dear. In essence, we are trying to achieve a *union*, and the most direct metaphorical connection to this is the act of sex.

As a physical sort of communion, it is no surprise that it can either bend or break a relationship, and even the Kama Sutra acknowledges that this is something to be aware of. According to their ancient traditions, people were and are guided by energies that inhabit the body – this is not a unique cosmological approach since many societies enculturate the idea of being 'in harmony' with powers or forces that defy the imagination. In the Indian tradition, however, this link between the spiritual and physical is best exemplified by the embodiment of the genitals. In Sanskrit, these were called 'lingam' (for the male reproductive system) and 'yoni' (for the female reproductive system) and were thought to represent the genitals of Shiva and his wife.

Understanding – and not being ashamed – of our genitals, and an appreciation for their uniqueness and for their ability to elicit pleasure in others is a profound and tangible form of happiness. And regarding them (not necessarily as the metaphorical organs of gods, per se) as something sacred is the first step in being able to share the experience of sex with a partner.

How To Get Started:

Before we get too hot and heavy, we want to start slow – sex is not 4

supposed to be a hasty or cathartic act, but something to savor. To this end, foreplay becomes a huge element of the sexual act, helping us to not only become comfortable with our own bodies and the bodies of our lovers but also stimulating physical arousal and fostering a sense of safety and intimacy.

Safety and Security are probably two of the most crucial elements between lovers – if you don't feel safe, if you are stressed or embarrassed, or more importantly if you're afraid of something, then sex can be a stifling and damaging process, and the union we spoke of will not be possible. Let's look at some of the concrete and specific ways we can include foreplay and create a safe space.

1. The Kama Sutra Embrace – this should always be the first thing lovers practice, and involves touching each other; however the word embrace doesn't just mean giving hugs, it means using your entire body to hold another person. Take turns among each other pressing and touching the other on their body, running your fingers along their arms, across their belly, over their chest, and down their legs. The idea here is to physically map one another's bodies. This helps bring a full *tactile awareness* to the one being touched but is also a good way to help build trust between partners. You can also try kissing one another, or brushing your lips across certain parts of the body – but the key here is gentleness; let your caresses be as soft as flower petals, and let your lover want more than what you're giving.

2. Kissing – the Kama Sutra is quite explicit about how kissing should be, and again gentleness is the key. The slower you are able to kiss, the longer you can draw out the process of foreplay,

12

and the more stimulated both lovers will become. This will also heighten arousal and make the actual act of sex all the more pleasurable. This is also, in a way, a sort of test of patience for both parties, and you are encouraged to seek out parts of the body that aren't normally considered "sexy" – for example, try kissing the inside of the elbow, the top of the scapula, the knee, etc.

3. Using Nails/Biting – varying the sort of tactile stimulus you deliver to your partner is also emphasized. For example, drawing your nails across their stomach, or allowing yourself to nibble parts of the body. Because the mouth is considered one of the most erogenous parts of the body, it is pleasurable for both people. In fact, there is an entire chapter devoted just to biting that includes such methods as:

- The Point – when skin is bitten with two teeth.

- The Coral and Jewel – when the lip and teeth are brought together when biting (the lip being the 'coral' and teeth being the 'jewel')

- Biting of the Boar – many broad bites with red spaces between.

d. Hidden Bite – when the only evidence is extensive red marks left by the teeth.

e. Line of Jewels – when all the teeth are used.

4. Sweet Nothings – in reality, being able to talk to your lover while engaging in intimacy isn't nothing at all, but *everything.* This relates a lot to what we call 'communal communication.' Being able to tell the other person what they want – or indeed, what they *don't* want – is something that many lovers sometimes have a hard time with, because they're afraid of not living up to expectations or letting the other person down. This is extremely important to overcome. If your foreplay is consistent and if your relationship is healthy, then there will be a lot of trust between partners, and both will be sensitive to the other's needs as well as their limitations. But when attempting something new (and experimenting is *great* for keeping the romance alive and for helping to push each other) always check your lover's respond and if in doubt always ask if what you're doing is okay.

5. External Stimulation – just as each person is unique and their preferences (sexually or otherwise) will differ, so too do our methods of arousal and stimulation. The Kama Sutra points out the necessity of trying to create a positive environment that is able to accommodate a feeling of good will and safety. Positive Sexual Environments

As mentioned, the Kama Sutra has a lot of chapters designed to elucidate the fact that love is not just a physical act, but also an intellectual and emotional one. While we would like to focus on the physical aspects, being able to develop an environment that is conducive to sexual trust is indispensable. Some suggestions include being able to fill your room with things that both of you love or that you can engage in both before and after – for example, books that you both like, a drawing pad, musical instruments, chess, or other activities that can accompany lovemaking.

It is also important that you both feel comfortable. Creating a 'nest' for yourselves that includes soft blankets, pillows, and fragrant candles can help produce a romantic atmosphere and put you both at ease (especially if you're trying something together for the first time).

Music can also be an aphrodisiac of sorts. But don't worry if you don't play and instrument yourself – having a soft slow-paced instrumental music playing in the background as you engage in foreplay is another great way to ease both lovers into the moment and help keep you at a gradual pace. Remember again, we're trying to savor the experience of one another, not rush through it!

Aquatic Is A No-No?

Another amusing aspect of the Kama Sutra is that Vatsyayana advocated that the best way to learn the following techniques and sexual positions was to practice them in water. There are some obvious logical reasons for this, especially ones that involve a lot of flexibility or strength (such as holding your lover up while making love, all at the mercy of gravity), and quite frankly we think it's a good idea. That said, Vatsyayana went on to clarify that there was a certain unethical or 'dirtiness' associated with copulating in water that tied in heavily to the spiritual and religious tenor of the day – while some of these taboos and customs may not make much sense today, and you are by no means tied to them, it's always good to know the historical context.

CHAPTER 2:
POSITIONS FOR HER

Sexual congress is rather unique in that the differences between men and women contributes to a variety of positions that benefit the woman. By 'benefit' we mean that certain activities are able to produce more stimulation for the woman *or* are easier for her to engage in. We'd like to look at a number of these that have been shown to be more popular among women, but will also delve into some of the most unique positions.

Before we begin though we should point out that the Kama Sutra goes further in describing women by classifying vaginas according to three categories. For a woman, it can be a doe, a mare, or a cow-elephant (yes, not the most flattering analogies) – however for our purposes, we can simply think of it as small, medium, and large. There is no stigma attached to either shape; each person is as unique as their genitals, and differences are to be celebrated. At the same time, certain positions, for men or women, can be more suitable for certain types of genitals. For example, some positions might be more difficult and even painful for those with a small vagina, but might be perfect in terms of those with larger vaginas.

The Balancing Act

This unique position tries to tap into a sort of primal energy in both man and woman. It is ideal for those that have a certain amount of endurance and flexibility since it requires strength from both. In essence, the man lies on his back with his legs apart. The woman then sits down between his thighs, her back to him, and allows for penetration. This is especially good for women who have a hard time reaching climax since it encourages a very deep penetration but most importantly gives the woman the ability to stimulate herself. While between his legs, she then wants to curl herself into a half fetal shape, with her knees up. It is the duty of the man to hold and support her there and is a good position to try in sequence with others since it puts the woman in control. From her perch, she can maneuver his penis inside her and direct the movements of the pair, but can also tease the man by touching or stroking his perineum.

Queen of Heaven

As we've seen, the sort of sexual position that is possible for men and women differs considerably depending on the variable sizes of penis and vagina. The Queen of Heaven is a position that requires a lot of practice, and is used to help those women whose vaginas are very narrow or "tight." It involves the woman lying on her back with her legs open; the man opens up her thighs with both hands and straddles his thighs on the *outside* of hers with his knees flat at her side. There are several variations to this practice, and at this point the man can either use his fingers to help ease open his lover's vagina or simply engage in penetration – it is very important to go slow with this position so as not to injure your partner or hurt her, and involves a lot of communication. It was originally designed to help women with smaller vaginas become more accustomed to sex but is also a good technique for women who naturally have a hard time having sex to help acclimate their vaginal muscles. This position is also known as Indranika and is named after the semi-mythical king of heaven Indra who composed this position as an ode to his wife.

The Hero

This is a great one for women as well, since it offers deep penetration and G-spot stimulation, but is easy for anyone. The woman lies on her back with her legs straight up in the air while the man kneels and enters her at an oblique angle – the woman can then scoot her butt further up so that it is resting on his thighs. This puts most of the work on the man and helps the woman avoid muscle cramps, but still gives a lot of satisfaction. Many couples also enjoy this position because it allows them to look at each other, but also offers itself to a variety of other interests and sexual preferences such as light BDSM: because the woman's legs are straight up, they can be tied together, or simply grasped by the man who can manipulate them at will.

The Amazon

If you really want to be in a position of power and trade-off the normal roles, the Amazon is a perfect position. In essence, it is a reversal: the man, instead of the woman, lies on his back with his legs spread apart. He then pulls his knees toward his chest so that it looks like he's sitting on a chair on his side – this makes room for the woman to come in and kneel down on top of him, her thighs resting on the bottom of his and her arms free to grip his calves or knees. This is a unique position in that it allows for a lot of movement from both lovers since the woman has the ability to rock back and forth quite a bit. The man pushes his penis between his legs so that it's underneath him and because the woman is on top it can be a very rewarding experience for the woman (and the closest thing to emulating what it would be like to be the man short of using a strap-on).

The Ape

A variation on the Amazon, this simply involves the woman sitting in the opposite direction – the man leans on his back with his knees drawn up at 45-degree angles and the woman maneuvers herself onto his erect penis, but this time faces *outward* (her back to him). Experimenting with the Ape versus the Amazon can be a fun and exciting way for the woman to decide which is more stimulating to her since both positions let her have the majority of control (i.e. motion, depth of penetration, rhythm).

Mixing Milk And Water

Similar to the Lotus position described below, this act again is super pleasurable for women by allowing them to control the overall movement and rhythm of sex. The man sits on a ledge, like the edge

of a bed for example, and the woman straddles him. This is ideal for lovers that want to be close together and to look at each other as they have sex. The man can also help support the woman by gripping her torso and breasts, or by her hips to encourage a synthesis of movement between them. The man may also further stimulate the woman by kissing and caressing her breasts as she works herself against him.

The Lotus

Perhaps one of the most iconic sex positions, this one again tries to foster trust and is one of the more intimate positions. It involves sitting facing each other in a half-cross legged position. The woman then straddles the man and both their legs splay out (from above the triangular angle of their legs look somewhat like petals, and the two lovers sitting straight up look like the rising flower of the lotus, hence the name of the position). This is actually a perfect blend of both woman and man being able to find purchase in the sexual act and is a great position to *end* on since there is a connoted sense of equality between lovers. For the woman, it is an opportunity to gaze into the eyes of your lover and to feel the real connection that occurs through eye contact – the proximity to one another can also lead to kissing on the mouth, as well as the breasts. And while there are other positions that still allow both people to look at one another, the Lotus is one of the few that brings them so close together – it also isn't a coincidence that a position like this which seems to embody emotional love and trust should be named after one of the more sacred plants in Indian and Buddhist thought (recall that the highest chakra in the spiritual- somatic philosophy is, in fact, the Lotus Chakra).

Additionally, many men and women alike prefer this as either the beginning or ending position because the proximity to one another's face also emphasizes moans of pleasure which can be extremely stimulating.

CHAPTER 3:
POSITIONS FOR HIM

Generally speaking, there is a big biological difference between men and women when it comes to sexual arousal – on average, there is a scientific basis for the fact that men can achieve arousal and orgasm easier than women. Women often require a slightly more protracted time to reach that optimum level, and it can be a source of conflict, contention, and embarrassment for the man and woman when neither body can arrive at the same time. As such, fair or not, it places a bigger responsibility on the man to help his lover achieve orgasm. Below we'll look at some positions that are pleasurable or beneficial to the men in a relationship, both regarding how they can synchronize sexually to their partners and how to best maintain a high level of intimacy while still eliciting desire and pleasure from the physical act.

Just as women in the Kama Sutra are classified according to the relative size of their vaginas, there is a gauge for men as well that categorizes penis size according to being a hare, a bull, or a stallion. Again, egos aside, there is no shame attributed to either size, since all three are able to accomplish different positions with different degrees of success – in the Kama Sutra, however, it does point out that there are certain compatibilities (for example, a woman with a doe – small – vagina may not be suited to a man with a stallion – large – penis), so it is important to consider each new position as to whether or not it will be possible or pleasurable for both lovers.

The Galley

This position gets the best of both worlds – for the man it is easy and doesn't involve too much flexibility, and for the woman it offers a lot of control and clitoral stimulation. The man lies on his back, and the woman straddles over him, with her back to him. She then leans far forward, which is perfect for hitting her G-spot, and she has the option of gripping the man's ankles to further support herself. For men who suffer from premature ejaculation this can also be a good position because most of the control is given to the woman who can rub her clitoris herself or grind it against her partner, while the man can focus his attention – *One excellent strategy that is also discussed for men who suffer from this is attempting to exercise their urinary muscles. The same muscles that control the contraction of urine can also be tightened and squeezed to help delay ejaculation and orgasm, but again open lines of communication between partners can also assist in drawing out the experience.*

The Crossed Keys

Perfect for men who have average or below average penis sizes (hare 18 or bull), this position puts you in control and is a good position for men who have a more difficult time reaching orgasm. The woman lies on her back with her hands behind her head and her legs straight up in the air while the man kneels down in front of her. The man can then grasp her ankles, and instead of *opening them* will cross them over one another like an X. This has the effect of squeezing her vagina tighter and increasing friction during penetration of the penis – the beauty of this technique however is that the man can control (somewhat) how "tight" his partner is by increasing the angle of her cross legs, with the smallest amount of degrees often resulting in a huge change. This way the man can control his own stimulation as well as his partners. *Note *that for women with a small vagina, this should be done very slowly and carefully and with permission – women might find this position uncomfortable, but the majority will also enjoy the added friction of penetration.*

The Laptop

Extremely pleasurable for the man, this position is also equable in giving a lot of control to the woman so she can manipulate her own progression toward orgasm. The man sits on a chair and woman sits facing him on his lap – her legs go over his shoulders and rest against the back of the chair. This position fosters a lot of trust and intimacy between lovers since they are facing so close to one another, and relies heavily on the man to support her as she works herself against him. Because her legs are up so high, it also offers a very deep penetration. A certain amount of fitness is required here to hold her in position, as she will be relying on you to keep her balanced.

The Splitting of Bamboo

A rather colorful metaphor, this rather easy-to-achieve position involves a little more flexibility. The woman lays on her side and raises one leg. The man can then approach and slide in parallel to her, allowing entrance to her vagina and straddling one leg on the bed while holding the opposing leg. This one again puts a lot of control in the hands of the man who can thrust back and forth at his leisure, as well as manipulate his partner's leg that's in the air. For women this can be a rather exciting new technique since it involves stimulation via the penis against areas of her vagina and vulva that doesn't usually get the same sort of attention, and because her legs are wide open it can also result in a significantly deeper penetration than the more standard man-on-top positions (the higher he lifts your leg, the deeper he can go).

Mare's Position

This is a technique that goes hand in hand with other positions, and is aimed at both increasing virility in the male and also helping to sustain a longer period of lovemaking. The most common practice is for the woman to lie on her back with her legs and knees raised to allow the man to kneel into her – once he is inside her though she grasps the shaft of his penis and holds it in her. One method of avoiding premature ejaculation is to cut off sensation to the tip of the penis where the majority of the nerve endings are located which lead to orgasm; this action of the woman grasping the penis (with practice from both partners) inside her can achieve the same effect. When he feels himself about to climax, she can grip his organ harder, cutting off the supply of blood to the penis, and resulting in longer endurance.

The Prone Tiger

Another relatively laidback position for both men and women, the man definitely gets the longer end of the stick this time (although the pun works better if it had been the woman!). Sitting straight up the man allows the woman to straddle him, first, with her back toward him. Then, she gently leans all the way forward so that her stomach is on the bed. This position gives the man full view of her buttocks and behind, and can be a rewarding experience for couples wanting to try something a little different – the man can then tease or rub her perineum, or grip her buttocks as they gyrate together, and the woman can further wrap her arms around her partner's feet. The arousal level of this position (in terms of the man being able to indulge in the site of his lover's genital region, and the woman being able to fully expose herself in a trust-filled environment) definitely makes it one of our favorites.

Blow of the Boar

Taking its cue from tantric techniques, this is a really good method for both bringing your partner to sexual readiness but is equally effective at helping to bring down passions after orgasm. The Blow of the Boar demonstrates a number of methods that don't involve penetration, but instead focus on rubbing the penis (or lingam) against a single part of the vagina (yoni) – more specifically, this is where the man can grind his organ against the labia majora or the clitoral hood and is particularly effective in making a woman 'wet' by exuding vaginal lubrication. A similar method, Blow of the Bull, allows the man to rub his entire penis against his partner's genitals and is a good warm-up or warm-down exercise. Ancient Penis Enlargers

It seems that no matter how far we progress as a race, certain things will always remain the same – and one of those is a persistent focus and obsessions with the size of genitals. Just as we are bombarded with junk emails these days telling us about secret ways to enlarge our penises, the Kama Sutra was by no means an exception to this. We wanted to include what Vatsyayana said about the issue, but by no means advocate his advice which involves utilizing the bodies/venom of the shuka, a forest-dwelling species of wasp.

"To increase the size and potential of the penis take shuka hairs and mix with oil and rub on the penis for ten nights...when a swelling appears sleep face downwards on a wooden bed, letting one's sex hang through a hole." – Vatsyayana, *Kama Sutra*

CHAPTER 4:
STRENGTH POSITIONS

We all know that sex is a sometimes grueling and rigorous physical act, but that's one of the reasons that it so appeals to us – the ability to work ourselves physically, with a partner, toward orgasm is one of the most rewarding experiences between couples. The Kama Sutra understand this fact very well, and many of the passages included in the original and compiled texts includes sexual positions designed to maximize stimulation through rigorous or strength-based sexual acts. Below we'll take a look at a few of them that make demands on both women and men.

The Sphinx

This one requires a lot of energy on behalf of the man, but its result is an almost ecstatic effect on the woman. The position involves the woman lying on her stomach and propping herself up on her elbows so that their torso is perpendicular to the bed. She stretches out one leg straight behind her, but then brings up the opposing leg to one side and crooks her knee – this makes her butt and vagina available to the man who slides in between and has to support himself on his arms. It can be very tiring, but well worth it if it means solving the Sphinx's riddle if you know what we mean.

Climbing The Vine

This tried and tested technique from the Kama Sutra requires both partners to be in good shape, and belongs to a category of forms that involve standing up. The man stands normally and embraces the woman who is required to lift her leg up and over his shoulder. This spreads her legs considerably, and offers very deep penetration, but can be exhausting for the woman over long periods of time, which means the man plays an important role in holding her up. There are other variants of Climbing the Vine that doesn't require the woman stretching her leg over his shoulder but only raised up (for example, the man holds her leg under the knee).

The Plough

There are a number of names for this one, but they all essentially mean the same, and this requires considerable strength on behalf of the man. The woman lies with half of her torso on a table or bed at waist height, and the man grips both her legs and enters from behind. This again offers good penetration because of its friction, but puts the man in control – it is recommended to hold the woman under her thighs for more support, and for the women to bend her legs at the knee to help him.

The Medusa

Another form that has many variants, this one again puts a lot of responsibility on the man but requires both partners to exercise considerable balance. Essentially the man squats on his heels – or if you're devoted to the technique, on his toes – and the woman straddles over top of him, 'sitting' on his lap in such a way that her feet touch the ground. Because of the cooperation required to make this position work (such that they don't tip over backward or forwards), many lovers find it to be tremendously intimate and can lead to a richer and fuller orgasm since both partners are embracing and clutching each other close during the interim.

Standing

In reality, 'standing' position is more like an umbrella term for a number of forms that have mutated over the years. One version of the standing – or *sthitarata* – position involves the man bucking up against the wall where he holds his lover. This can involve straddling or wrapping her legs around him or, as a way to spice things up and get you really sweating, the male supports the woman's feet in his palms while the woman clings either to his neck or chest. This involves the woman having to pull her knees up to her chest (and his) in an almost fetal position. While extremely taxing on both parties, the end result can be a very powerful and synchronous orgasm.

Related to this is another variation on the standing posture. This again has the man with his back against the wall and holding the woman. The woman this time, however, presses her feet flat against the vertical wall while her partner helps to support her, either under the thighs or (more commonly) by the waist. This can be an extremely rigorous technique as well and involves trust on behalf of both partners, but especially the man. This unique position – *avalambitaka* – also grants the woman a lot of control and freedom since she can control and guide the rhythm by pressing off the wall or bending her knees.

Supernova

Not necessarily a classic Kama Sutra move, this modified (and modern) technique still requires a lot of technical expertise and can result in some very enthusiastic love-making. The man lets his abdomen and legs remain on the bed, but lets his upper torso incline backward (much like the Waterfall move but reversed for women) – the woman then crouches above him on the bed and allows herself to take him at her convenience. This one is a good combination of strength and flexibility because the man has to support himself without falling off the bed, and the woman tends to take control in a squatting position.

Suspended Scissors

Similar to the Plough, this position requires strong forearms and biceps from the woman. She places both hands initially flat on the ground; the man, now standing, then wraps one of her legs between his own and grips the other leg in front of him. This 'cross-lateral' penetration can be great for the woman because it enhances clitoral stimulation and exposure to her labia. As an added challenge, the

woman can then raise one arm to support the man who is holding her suspended – as you can imagine if you can't do at least a few push-ups this technique can be a killer but is a fun one to try.

Squat Balance

A similar take on some of the suspended congress moves, this one involves the man standing while the woman stands on a bed and arches her knees/legs at a 45-degree angle – as if she were sitting on a chair.

The man is able to penetrate her at an upward angle and support her buttocks, and she can rest on his arms. An excellent technique for building trust between partners, but be sure the man in this situation has strong arms since most of the work of movement and rhythm will be up to him.

The Spin

Also called *paravrittaka*, this is an especially inventive sexual position that requires both flexibility and strength, as well as good timing and communication with one's partner. There have been a number of modern mutations (such as the Helicopter), but the original Kama Sutra posture involves the man sitting with his legs straight out in front of him; the woman kneels on his lap with her back to him, and at this point, they can both work with each other. However, the kicker comes when the woman – with her lover still inside her – executes a 180 and turns all the way around so that she is facing him. As one would except Vatsyayana cautions adventurous couples to be careful with this one so as not to injure themselves, and the Kama Sutra remarks that there are few who can pull this off – although, it *does* mention that lesbians can accomplish this with greater ease. There is definitely a degree of obviousness in that statement.

Lower Congress

Although the majority of the Kama Sutra focuses exclusively on foreplay and vaginal penetration, but it does include a few more "aberrant" forms of congress, most notably anal sex. The pictures and descriptions listed in the *Kama Sutra* are quite formal despite their insinuations, with translations suggesting that "an ingenious person should multiply the kinds of congress after the fashion of the different kinds of beasts and of birds." We can summate the best position for both man and woman as being that which resembles a bull taking his mate – and can translate this pretty clearly as the woman lying on her knees and pressing her face into a soft pillow while the man takes her from behind.

CHAPTER 5:
FLEXIBILITY POSITIONS

In reality both strength *and* flexibility go hand in hand, and there are historical interpretations and connexions in the Kama Sutra that seem indicative of yoga influences – but essentially, whether it's strength or flexibility that defines a particular sexual position, the aim is the same: to increase stimulation and desire by pushing the body to its limit. The physiological effect of 'pushing the borders' is what is often referred to as a liminal reaction, that is, an experience that results in a spiritual and ecstatic realization.

Now, whether or not you have a religious awakening during sex aside, there is definitely an empirical basis for athletes undergoing a sense of altered or heightened awareness when pushed to the physical limit. So why shouldn't sex be able to accomplish the same thing? We've seen some strength-oriented sex positions, so let's take a look at some ones that require flexibility (and keep in mind that many of these are the sort you have to *practice* and work up to and are not necessarily for everyone!)

The Waterfall

We'll start off easy: the waterfall is similar to other variations we've seen and involves the man sitting on a chair with the woman propping herself on his lap to achieve penetration. The difference here is that the woman then bends backward down the man's legs so that her head is upside down. This can be very pleasurable for both partners since the man can stroke her stomach, breasts, and genital regions, while the woman allows herself to fall backward in the imitation of a waterfall – this mainly requires flexibility from the woman since she is essentially arching her back all the way back.

Reclining Pigeon

Not a terribly difficult position, this pose puts the woman on her back again. She brings up one knee, and then slides her opposing leg over top of it (you'll know you've got the position because of the pull in your gluteus maximums) – threading her arms under the leg on top, she uses both hands to clutch her other leg. By pulling up, she can manipulate the access to her vagina, and is a good equality technique – while the man approaches from the top and can initiate a rhythm, the woman is able to control the degree of friction by pulling up to enlarge the opening to the vagina.

Note this position is very good by itself at helping to relieve muscle tension in the rump area, but be careful about using it in sexual congress if you are stiff as it is very easy to pull this muscle.

The Shoulder Stand

Another position that seems right out of a yoga book this technique relies on the woman to have a strong back; she lies on her back, and the man stands on his knees. Gripping her by the waist he guides her up to his penis and, with her help, begins to enter her. The reason this position is so tricky is that it involves the man having to hold her up, and the woman is required to bend her back by almost 45 degrees in order to sustain the posture, which can leave you both sweating in no time at all.

The Mill Vanes

A very intimate and relatively moderate position, the mill vanes technique is a favorite of couples since it is a somewhat unusual position, yet manages to satisfy a considerable amount of clitoral stimulation. The woman lies on her back and then the man straddles over top of her (as one would do to initiate 69 oral sex). However, the man then leans all the way forward so that his penis can penetrate his partner – the angle of this coitus can be a fresh experience for both lovers but may require a few tries to get right. The man leans all the way forward on his stomach, and the woman can help assist with this technique by folding her legs over the small of his back. For the woman, this can be a unique opportunity to get a glimpse of her lover's rump while having sex and can entice external stimulation by using her hands to caress his buttocks, thighs, or testicles.

The Bridge

Hailed as one of the more difficult Kama Sutra techniques to pull off – and usually not for long – the bridge makes a flexibility demand on the *man* this time. In a pose that will be familiar to yoga enthusiasts, the man creates an arc by leaning back so that his hands and feet are flat on the ground, and his stomach/chest is facing outwards. Just to achieve the base position can be strenuous, but once the man is ready, the woman kneels over top of his penis and inserts it into her vagina. She can then ride on top of him, stroking his chest or fondling his perineum – additionally, the positions can actually be reversed with the woman acting as the 'bridge.' In this case, the woman bends all the way back and arches her stomach toward the ceiling while the man gently clutches her by the waist to enter her. This can be amazingly seductive and arousing for the man for the same reason as the woman in the reversed position since he can stroke her stomach and breasts. For the woman, it is also easier since she doesn't have to worry about supporting her partner's weight as he is coming in from the side rather than straddling her.

Note it is a good idea for the woman to try and support as much of her weight as possible when the man is the 'bridge' in order to avoid injuring her partner or adding undue stress – this can sometimes be an issue with partners who are not equitable in height.

Fixing of the Nail

And we're back to the woman again; this position was even pointed out by Vatsyayana as requiring a special amount of practice given its crobatic nature. The woman needs to bring one of her feet up to her head (think of someone trying to smell their own foot or bite their own toe), and then extend the other leg out in front of her. The man can then approach and enter her at her discretion – the result is one of the deepest penetrations, but requires a lot of flexibility. Because of its dynamics, it's also a good exercise for women with smaller or "tighter" vaginas because it will help ease open the vaginal passage and allow a smoother and more pleasant entrance of the penis.

The Crab Position

Another favorite, this one can be achieved by most women but still requires a degree of flexibility. The woman lies on her back again but this time brings up her legs and tries to place her feet on her abdomen. With her legs contracted and placed on her stomach she can then push her arms under her knees to support them in that position – this opens up her vagina to allow her partner to penetrate. The benefit of this position is that it easily accommodated women who have all sizes of vaginas: for those with tighter entrances, the woman can simply open her arms and thereby spread her vagina wider. For women with larger vaginas, the opposite motion can be achieved by tucking in her arms and creating a smaller opening, which will increase friction and lead to a more pleasurable congress for both partners. This position is a nice balance between control, granting the man the 'upper' position by allowing him to guide and choose the rhythm and movement, but also allowing the woman to control the intensity of the sex.

The Rowing Boat

For those who want all the comfort and security of being able to face their partners with the added ability to maintain eye contact, then the Rowing Boat definitely fits the bill. This is a medium variety position in terms of flexibility, but offers some great support and requires good open communication (although it might take a few tries to get into a steady rhythm). Both partners face each other, and the man lies down to start – the woman may descend onto him until the penis is fully inserted, and then the man sits up again, so he is facing her. The man places his knees on the outside of her body, and she does the same, resulting in a sort of crossed leg situation. This is a very comfortable position, however, because partners can support themselves and the other by gripping their partner's legs. Since the knees of both partners are raised (and at chest level), it maximizes the amount of genital surface area for both – the man and the woman can then rock back and forth against each other, and while this position does not allow for a lot of external/internal movement of the penis in and out of the vagina, the opportunity to have both genital areas rubbing against one another makes this one of the more *stimulating* techniques for couples.

Dog Poses

Many yoga poses actually double as effective sexual postures as well (though don't tell Vatsyayana that). The dog poses – Downward Facing Dog being the most popular – involves the woman putting both her hands and feet flat on the ground and making a V with her body (the inverse of the Bridge); this allows easy access to the man who can enter her at her discretion. A variation of this is the Three- Legged Dog Pose which involves the woman lifting up one of her legs straight in the air so that it is lined up with her spine – think of trying to make the shape of the Greek letter Lambda with your body. Both positions require flexibility from the woman and give a significant amount of control and power to the man (which may become a preference for couples that enjoy domination scenarios).

The last variation on this we want to discuss is what it is called the Standing Straddle Forward Bend – more than just a mouthful; this could be an incredibly erotic position for either man or woman. In the traditional yoga pose, the woman in a standing position spreads her feet so that there is considerable width between them. Then, slowly, she bends over and grasps both her ankles. At this point, the man can come in behind her and control her hips with his hands. The exposure level of this position is very high, so it's very important that partners have already established a significant degree of trust.

CHAPTER 6:
RELAXING POSITIONS

While there is something to say about spicing up one's sex life by incorporating new and wild techniques and positions, at the same time we're not all acrobatics – in the same vein, that aforementioned 'spice' of life really is variety. In fact, the Kama Sutra is quick to point out that mastering a diverse array of different positions is ideal not only for keeping things interesting but also in terms of experimenting and opening one's self up sexually. The ability to try new things helps to broaden our horizons, and since you are entering this new realm with a partner, it can also be a very satisfying journey of self-discovery (and discovery of the other person).

That said, switching things up and allowing yourself to occasionally revert to simpler forms or positions, or at least ones that aren't super physically demanding, can give you and your partner a diverse repertoire of experiences to choose from. In previous chapters we've experimented with flexibility, strength, and gender-specific positions; now we'd like to end with some easy, relaxing sexual techniques.

Child Pose

Another borrowed pose from yoga, and a relaxing and spiritual cathartic one, is the child pose – this involves the woman sitting on her knees and then stretching forward with both her arms. This elegant and tender position allows the man to come in behind and enter her, and can also prostrate himself in a similar child pose, this time leaning forward *over her body*. This can be very relaxing and a good one to try even after orgasm as it helps to stabilize and activate the parasympathetic nervous system.

Ananda Balasana

Not strictly a sexual position either, this is a very easy and relaxing pose that can be pleasurable to the woman – the woman lies on her back and attempts to bring her feet up as high as she can, whereby she grabs them with her hands. Think of a baby trying to grab its toes. Luckily, most women can do this without much difficulty, and it doesn't require an undo amount of flexibility to achieve, but *does* produce a deep penetration all the way to the G-spot. Remember to keep eye contact with your partner to maintain this level of intimacy – the natural 'spring' created by the woman having her legs up in the air also produces an innate rhythm which can be pleasing.

Zen Pause Sex

A bit of a modern take on the idea of tantric sex, the Zen pause sex position is something you can integrate into a number of different positions, especially the more vigorous ones. In this position both partners are lying facing each other – we like to suggest this one when one or both of you are nearing climax. But instead of driving through with the orgasm, you both turn on your sides and hold each other (the man preferably being able to stay inside his partner as they collapse, and the woman wrapping or entwining her legs around him). This can help couples that have a hard time with endurance or premature ejaculation by giving you a chance to strengthen your resolve – holding each other and letting the orgasm dwindle, then building up speed and passion again can result in huge orgasms for both, and is a great technique for bringing multiple orgasms to the woman.

Close-Up, or Womb Embrace

This can be exercised as an actual sex position or as a comfortable and intimate position after orgasm. Both man and woman lie in a classic spooning position but pull their legs up as far as they can to their chest – this makes the woman's rump extremely accessible to the man who can literally 'fold' around her form. At the same time, he can wrap his arms around her and kiss her neck and is a method we encourage men to adopt because it is a romantic and tender way to show a partner that they are loved. With so much body contact, it is a great way to open up one's energy and results in an extremely intimate blending – in the yoga tradition this could be compared to some methods of breath control like *pratiloman* that try to mimic a 'going back,' a way to relive what it was like to be in the womb. So you can see why this is such a powerful technique: the man in this context becomes like a metaphorical womb for his partner, nurturing an overwhelming sense of safety and security.

Reclining Lotus

If you haven't guessed yet, there are a lot of ways to improve or experiment with fundamental positions, and the Reclining Lotus can combine the intimacy level of the sitting Lotus with a somewhat more casual approach, especially if the woman is tired. The position involves the woman lying on her back and then crossing her legs as she would have done with the Lotus position, but this time the man enters her in a standard missionary style, with her legs pressing against his chest. Aside from giving the woman a break, the action of crossing her legs also produces a natural 'spring,' so this technique can create a very fluid sense of rhythm during congress.

Reclining Bend Angel

Another reclining position, this one is good to help increase endurance and extend the process of lovemaking. The woman lies on her back and brings both of her arms up above her head, holding both palms together. Not only does this help stretch out her abdomen, but can also produce a very sexy curve in her posture – next she brings her legs up and attempts to touch both soles together. This involves forcing her knees down and outward, and therefore should only be attempted by a partner who is limber enough to do this without hurting herself (the knees should be able to touch the floor in this position). Finally, the man comes in and straddles over top of her, making sure not to disturb her legs so that they remain in formation. With his knees on either side, he can dip into her vagina from a steep angle, creating an incredible amount of friction.

CONCULSION

Throughout the last six chapters we've looked at a variety of elements related to Kama Sutra, everything from the philosophical framework that led to the development of the text (including the sacredness attached to the 'lingam' and 'yoni') to the importance of foreplay in both exciting and reproducing an environment and atmosphere of *trust*. The ability to share one's self – both emotionally and physically – is the hallmark of the Kama Sutra.

In our modern age, however, the Kama Sutra offers up another opportunity: to enliven our sex lives by engaging in positions that may seem unorthodox (and downright difficult!). But therein lies the beauty of it. Sex, like any other activity, and especially one that involves another person, requires *practice*. The ability to master a new sexual position is an enthralling moment for both partners.

Whether you're a new couple who are only beginning to explore each other's sexuality, or you've been together with someone for a long time, this book has hopefully opened your eyes to the exotic possibilities offered by tantric sex. But even though we've focused mainly on the physical components of lovemaking, it's useful (and healthy) to realize that any relationship must function on a number of levels in order to sustain itself and flourish.

We hope you've enjoyed – and taken something away – from this book that you will be able to share and practice with your own partners. We also hope that no matter what, this book has at least demonstrated the necessity of keeping an open mind. After all, relationships are the most beautiful of adventures, and sex should be embraced with that same sensibility!

SEX POSITIONS FOR COUPLES

COUPLES

The Orgasm Bible

The ultimate guide to finally getting the sex life you always dreamed of with your partner

Author: JESSICA ANDERSON

INTRDUCTION

When it comes to sex, the sex scene should be a fascinating and captivating one, though the longer people are in relationship a pattern is form especially when it comes to their self life. Partners sometimes find self doing one sex position over and over again. Well, one of the couple might find that regimen boring and want to step up to keep things new, spicy and refreshing in the bedroom, which is really how things with sex need to be with couples. It is fitting for couples to sometimes live and breathe experimental sex to bring forth a better connectivity with the partner. Behavioral scientist and relationship coach, Clarissa Silva opined that sex positions shouldn't be static for partners that need to connect for a long time in a relationship, but sex positions should always be learned, explored and practiced in the course of every connection. A lot of couples have put off their sexual flames just because of boring and monotonous sex positions which have made one of the partners looks else way to get the satisfaction and experimental sex he or she has always craved for.

Sex positions which are those positions of the body that people use for sexual intercourse or other sexual activities should be flexible, the fact remains that in an excellent sexual relationship a partner will want to learn and absorb all thing that pleases the other partner every time they both have sex, so that as the relationship evolves both partners will be in tandem, making it easier to be intuitive about one another sexual needs. The beauty of this is that you won't have to bargain what you need any longer because your partner will act on it. So sometimes you might not be lucky to have a partner that is experimental with sex positions but if not all hope is not lost. Aforementioned is why we have put together this book to help such couples out.

This comprehensive book on sex positions for couples is here for people that feel like the lost connection with their partners; maybe it seems that the feeling of deep connection you both had before now has disappeared and you need to put it all back immediately. You want to become a master at being able to create a connection with powerful sexual feelings. Peradventure, you have been looking out to learn stimulating and passionate sex positions that will put back the sexual flames back into your relationship. Then your best bet is to read this book.

This book is here for you to try new sex positions to help you dump the old missionary sex position, especially if monotony as really get in the way of your bedroom romp. You will be able to learn from this book that there are plenty of other positions you can try to heat things between the sheets. This book is for young and old, male and female, learners and amateurs that need to put back life into their bedmatics. This book is a whole package to help make your sex life wilder, hotter and orgasmic.

According to Sheena LaShay an intellectual sensual Shaman, wild, magical woman and cultural provocateur opined that one could have the best lover in the world who knows how to please one with unlimited supply of stamina, energy, and sexual curiosity, but if the other partner thinks that one only accepts or allow a particular or just sex positions as the case may be then one will be intentionally limiting one's capacity to pleasure from the numerous tantalizing sex positions that abound. So the problem has always been lack of exposure, fewer experimentation skills, being used to a particular sex position, and lack of adventurous mind, religious belief, ethics, and behavioral pattern.

There are a lot of things you will learn from reading this masterpiece on sex positions for couples you will be able to determine the most comfortable sex positions that will require little energy that will be great for your spontaneous, sudden or unplanned sex. You will know the sex positions that will give you and your partner's great intimacy because they will enable you both hug each other during the process and there will be an opportunity of looking into each other eyes that will spark more sexual flames. This book will enable you to learn sex positions that will be exciting for your partner as a man and for the woman to receive some significant thrusting and a whole-body experience and these sex positions can be done quietly as well even if there are other people around. You will acquire the knowledge about sex positions that can dramatically lengthens the amount of time you can have intercourse with your partners too, how to stimulate your partner to orgasm and also watch your penis slide in and out of your partner which is like a major turn-on for a man and how best you can reach your woman's G-spot which can give the woman the needed cervical orgasms.

This book promises to explain the sex positions very visually so that you will vividly picture all the sex positions in your mind eyes as you read and be able to apply them to your sex life as you learn about each sex position. You will be sure of getting the best tips on each sex positions to set your sexy time on fire; this book will expressly outline the adventurous sex positions that will help keep your sex life super hot and take your sex life to another level.

So have you been looking for a book that explains the different goal-oriented sex positions vividly, that will deeply connect you to your partner and take you to the next level on the freakier side of you and your partner, then you need to grab this book now. The aforementioned is not just about the sex positions but passionate ones that would blow your mind and help put back the spark in your relationship. Get this book on sex position for couples, and I bet that you would be glad you did.

CHAPTER 1:
WHY THERE'S NEED FOR SEX AND THE USE OF DIFFERENT SEX POSITIONS IN A RELATIONSHIP

• Sex and sex positions

Sex might means different things to different people but the bottom line is that it is a very healthy and natural activity that everyone enjoys and find meaningful even with all the different meaning by different people. Sex is not just about vaginal intercourse; sex can be anything that feels sexual which could be vaginal sex, anal sex, hugging, kissing, oral sex or any sexual touching. Sexual activities are very important in a relationship whether one is straight, a lesbian, and bisexual, queer or gay or in any kind of sexual relationship. So basically, sex is any sexual activities that we engage in with our partners for sexual pleasure and gratification. We all know that there will come a time that it might become boring or like a routine if we do not spice things up and this is where sex positions comes into play.

Sex positions are the different sultry styles and ways of having orgasmic sex, sex positions should be used just like outfits where different ones should be used at different times. Imagine having sex that makes it looks like you are in your honey moon stage all the time. This is possible if you are acquainted with all the sex positions and its techniques. The fact is that with this, you wouldn't be able to keep your hands away from each other. You will always be horny and in the mood for intense orgasmic sex, filled with passion and deep connection and of course this will make you fall in love with your partner all over again.

• Tips and tricks to help you love adventurous sex positions

It is one thing is to know about the different hot pleasurable sex positions and orgasmic thrilling styles that can be adopted in the bedroom but the hardest part is being in the mood to explore and to try the suggestions and the new ideas out. The fact is that stepping up and trying something new might be terrifying, scary or uncomfortable for you but there are a lot of ways you can help raise yourself to your sexual height to stop sex drought. If you always need loud moaning, the bed squeaking and having passion sex with your partner then you need to use and love different sex positions. Because it is only this way that you will be able to heighten the fire, the excitement, passion and mind-blowing orgasm that have diminished in your sex life. So to rediscover your lost sexual desires and yearning for having sizzling sex. You can follow the under listed tricks and tips to get yourself to always be in a best mood for new steaming sexual positions.

• Get yourself a sexy masseur or masseuse

So you can get yourself in the mood by first wearing a kinky or sexy stuff to be more attractive, and then ask your partner to use hot oils to give you good soothing massages all over the body. This will help to reduce tension and as tension reduces from all part of your muscles, it will put you in a better mood to try your new sultry sex suggestions and positions.

• Keep installing the sex ideas in your mind

You will find yourself horny and needing good sex when you keep seeing an erotic sex picture in advance and how you will be having explosive sex under the sheet when you try out some very kinky sex positions. Make some noises, say sensual things and whisper sweet nothings in your partner ears ahead of time. Just go all naughty with your partner and talk dirty to prepare your mind for some very crazy sex positions that you will be expecting from your partner in the bedroom. All these will add up and make you want to try out hot sex positions and be in love with them.

• Spring up a surprise anywhere

There is something sensual and steamy about having a surprise sex anywhere else in the house especially in the shower and a lot of couples likes sexual encounters in the shower, so you can skip the boring bedroom routine for the time being and try other places and most importantly the shower. Surprise your partner maybe in the shower with erotic kisses, demand some fingering from your partner and totally move your hands all over your partner's body and let your partner's reciprocate same till you get in the mood.

• Flirt and play around with your partner

You can get yourself in the mood for some kinky sex in advance by sending suggestive but subtle text messages to your partner to let him or her know what's on your mind. You can flirt with sending romantic and sex appeal messages to their phone; you can also sound naughty and dirty as possible to give them a clue about your moves. All of these will add to make your sexual advances more persuasive and alluring to your partner and they will respond in a crazy way that will put you in the kind of sex mood you needed.

• Take the initial sex initiative

No need waiting for your partner to be in sexual mood by his or her self, because this route might take longer than you thought. Your partner might not be vocal about it but he or she will definitely appreciate if you take the bold step. You need to supercharge in the bedroom and then create a sexy atmosphere around your partner, he or she would feel aroused and attracted to your body. So go ahead and let them know you are really for sex with them and introduce the sex position you want to try out.

• Introduce porn videos

This could be the key you need to arouse yourself and be in the mood for a new sex position. Porn videos helps to introduce new sizzling sex positions and how to use them, there are a lot of porn videos now you can stream online or download to watch, just get the ones in accordance with your sex fantasies and you can watch it with your partner together. Watching the porn videos together can instantly arouse your partner and you both can practicalize what you are watching or just watched immediately, this will even help to make the experience more adventurous.

• Raise your self confidence

Sometimes you might feel insecure and may have low self esteem and this might lead to you not having physical connection with your partner. You will need to work on this aspect of your sexual life. so you need to remind him constantly that you have a banging body, that your partner will still find your body irresistible and hot, apparently, you need to keep arousing him or her with hot kisses, fondling, cuddling etc to make them feel desirable by you too. So all these will help you be desirable by partner and your partner will also be irresistible to you too and which will open you up to try out the new sex positions you have in your head.

- Outstanding gains of using different sex positions in a relationship

If all you think is a kiss and quickie after a long day of work that will just satisfy your partner, then you are in lalaland because your partner thinks sex with you is very boring. Your sex life should be explosive that of fun, passion, multiple orgasm and thrills. Your bedmatics skills should be hot and irresistible that your partner will love and be eager to be part of, and as such it always good to spice up your sex life to ignite the gone chemistry or heightened the passion that already exist. So it is expedient for you and your partner to learn how to unstuck from a sexual routine that must have engulf your sex lives. Give different sex positions a shot to kill boredom that will aid to spark the sexual flames and ignite all the intense feelings for love making. You might not have known but the below points are some killer reasons why you should learn and try out different sex positions in your sex life.

• It will emotionally connect you both

Nothing beats the good old benefits of emotionally connection with a partner after having fantastic bomb sex with one another. You two will stay connected to one another; there will be this subjective feeling that will bond both of you together. This kind of connection will help to arouse strong feelings which will enable you to value mind and soul of your partner and makes you have deep and meaningful conversations with them.

• It will increase intimacy

Introducing new sex positions in the bedroom all the time will keep away unfriendliness and aloofness from partners, so to have a moment of greatest pleasure or rush of sexual excitement with your partner. You must know how to keep things spicy and hot in the bedroom. Good amount of intimacy is needed to keep the connection very strong.

• It offers immense sexual pleasure

Working with some new ideas and sexual suggestions will make you and your partner rediscover your selves, this is like finding the best options that will build on already existing pleasurable zones. By trying new sex position you will discover more pleasurable options you will have to explore and of course the end result is more excitement and enjoyment during sex et al. Again, this will enhance deep penetration for the man and a better thrusting for the woman and these add up to make the sex experience heavenly. This is like finding both G-spot and what can give you both the ultimate satisfaction.

• Easy orgasm for the partners

Nothing is as frustrating as not being able to climax, in fact it shouldn't have a place in your bedroom or a very abnormal thing to experience. I believe orgasm is an experience that no couples want to exclude from their sex session because this is the explosive part of love making and it helps couples to love themselves better after a wow sex session. So using different sex positions in the bedroom can actual help you achieve this explosion effortlessly. It is all about going with the ideal positions and ideas that will give the best result. Of course if one doesn't experiment with the sultry positions learned, it might be counter-productive if one only gets to know about them without exploring and experimenting with them.

• It makes couples to be flexible

Knowing different sex positions and willingly to use them enable you to have several and numerous sex options to explore. Switching things up in the bedroom using the different sexual suggestions provided here will help spice up things in the bedroom. This will help you and your partner stop seeing sex as a routine or chore that needs to be done for the sake of it but what they look forward to having for immense pleasure, getting freaky and exploring another pleasurable zones. Using different sex positions available will make sex for couples or partners be more of a necessity and what should be done to make life more alluring for partners.

CHAPTER 2:
ORGASMIC SEX POSITIONS FOR BEGINNERS

Even though you are new to good sex making you can still become a master in the game if you are willingly to learn magnificent sex position that will leave you and your partners gasping for breath after each sizzling sex session. You can boost your sexual confidence and lovemaking skills in a short amount of time. There are great positions that you start using with your partner that will enable both of you to always be in the mood for intense pleasurable sex and thereafter have multiple orgasms.

You can introduce these 10 orgasmic sex positions to your sex sessions to have mind-blowing and explosive orgasm as a beginner to make your sex life come alive and remain spicy for a very long time.

• The folding chair sex position

If you want to show your partner your sex skill as a beginner in exploring the different sex positions you fantasized about then you can start with the folding chair sex position. This is a sizzling sex position that is easy to perform but gives an amazing result of multiple orgasms for both partners. This position will leave you moaning and asking for more because it's a position that the clitoris will easily accessed and the man can have a deep thrusting that will be sending tingling sensation down his spine for each thrust. With this sex position the woman lies on her back and lift her legs straight on the man's shoulder, then the man lower himself on the woman and insert his penis into the woman, but before then the man can do a bit of foreplay like fingering, dry humping, kissing and sucking. The man can start thrusting from that angle. To heighten the pleasure the man can make his pubic bone lean down with a bit of pressure on the woman clitoris. This will arouse the woman the more, making the partners have awesome sensual experience.

• Sexual spooning sex position

Sexual spooning sex position is one erotic sex position that brings exciting sensation and multiple orgasms during a sex session even as beginners. This sex position makes the man have adrenaline rush while affording the woman the opportunity of getting highly stimulated on her G-spot so that she will be moaning and screaming in ecstasy. If you are looking to give your partner spines tingling orgasm and out of breath ecstasy as you both continue to explore one another body then the sexual spooning sex position is the best bet. With this sex position the woman lie in front of the man while the man lies behind the woman, they would both be in a cuddling form. The man will penetrate the woman from behind. The man can use his free hands to grab the woman's breast to fondle it and reach out to suck it as well. The man can now start thrusting in and out while the woman can lift her leg a bit intermittently so that the man can be hitting on her clit from time to time. The man can make the woman let out all kind of pleasurable sounds by reaching forward to suck her clit, then penetrate and thrust harder again till the both climax in multiple orgasm.

• Cowgirl sex position

If you need a sizzling sex position that would enable you be in control of your own pleasure as a woman while pleasuring your man, then the cowgirl sex position will make your sex fantasy a reality. This steamy sex position always set the body ablaze with frenzy excitement; as it allow you and your partners explore your body to no end. This sex position enables the partners ride themselves to the seventh heavens in pleasure. Cowgirl sex position begins with the man laying on his back, then the woman get on top and lower herself onto the man, she sit up straight and direct the man's cock into her vagina and she can start grinding by moving forth and back. To give the man intense pleasures she can be intermittently sucking the cock and inserting it back into her vagina. To pleasure herself more she can lean backward which will allow for even deeper penetration and also enable the clitoris to rub hard on the cock. The woman can continue grinding and rocking the man and letting the sensation build up and she might now go a bit harder still the both explode in multiple orgasms.

• The double worm sex position

If you are looking to make you and your partner have steamy sex session together for optimal sexual pleasure and onward sexual orgasm, then going with the double worm sex position will be the best bet. This is one sex position that both partners can enjoy great stimulations on the genitals and a great way of making your fantasized dreams of having a hot sex session a reality. This sex position is very good for beginners, it very easy to try out and it helps direct partners on a better angle that will enable them hit on one another erogenous zones to elicit the immense pleasure needed. This position will have the woman lying on her back and the man will lie on his stomach on top of the woman's back, this should look like both partners are trying to do the worm. The man keeps his stomach resting on the woman's back, the woman can now lift her butt so that the man can penetrate from behind, and this will first send shivers down the woman spines because the pressure of the man inserting the penis will be rubbing against the clitoris making the thrusting sweeter. The woman can also help the man build up orgasmic sensation by giving the man a hand job. A rabbit vibration can be thrown in here for deep stimulation and more stimulation of all women's sexual spots. The man can go all freaky with actually sucking the woman vagina too, using the rabbit again before returning to insert the penis for diverse ways of building more sensation before the both explode in orgasm.

• Reverse cowgirl sex position

Reverse cowgirl sex position is a lovely sex position for beginners because it very simple but classic. So if you want to experiment with an easy sex position that will make you and your partner never to keep your hands off one another then go with this sex position. It will really give you both heavenly sensations that will see you both moaning and screaming in excitement. This sex position still has the man lying on his back like in the normal cowgirl position but the woman will be on top but with her ass facing the man. The position will enable the woman ride the man comfortably and the woman G-spot will be easily accessed. To heighten the pleasure and build more orgasmic thrills the man can lean forward and hold the woman waist so that she can bounce deeper on the cock, which will elicit intense pleasure for the partners. The woman can then move further up the man face and sit on it to be sucked before mounting the penis again. The view of the woman's booty moving back and forth is already an erotic sight for the man, which will definitely drive him crazy before climaxing and exploding like a volcanic eruption.

• Pillow talk sex position

You can never go wrong using the pillow talk sex position with your partner even as a beginner in the game of exploring other sex positions that will give you and your partner immense pleasure and orgasmic explosions during your steamy sex session. Pillow talk sex position is an awesome sex position that will be sexually fulfilling for both partners. This sex position enable the partners hit directly on the each other erotic spots especially the woman's G-spot allowing the man pubic bone to rub against the girl's clitoris. Pillow talk sex position is one sex position that is great for beginners that need some easy to maneuver sex positions and are straightforward to use. Pillow talk sex position begins with the woman laying on her back and putting a fluffy pillow under her ass to help lift her ass off the bed to aid better penetration from the man. The man gets on top of the woman, but before then the man can give the woman some fingering, rubbing of the clits, sucking the clit and also getting a blowjob from the woman. The man can now penetrate the woman while the woman wraps her legs round the man's waist for extra depth and deep penetration. To build up more sensation and intense pleasure, the man can part the woman's labia apart so that his body rubs directly against the woman's clitoris to heighten the pleasure. Lastly, the man can go back to thrusting in and out then the both reach orgasm.. With this position the partners are sure of satisfying their desires perfectly.

- **The stand up position sex position**

The stand up position is a perfect sex position for beginners; It one sex position that will enable newbie's experience volcanic orgasms if they have never had it so good before. It gives room for both partners to discover all the sensual and erotic spots on their body which will give them heavenly pleasure. This sex position will always leave the partners asking for more as the pleasure one another. Stand up sex position come with a difference, it begins with the man standing in front of the woman and facing her while the woman sit at the edge of the bed and spread her legs. The man lean forward to get a good blowjob from the woman while he fondle with the woman breast as well as touching the other erogenous zones on the woman's body . The man will now lower himself to penetrate the woman from the standing angle which will enable him have a good view of the woman's G-spot which will drive him crazier. A sex toy can be introduce at this point to help stimulate the woman's G-spot even more too

for both partners and the man can later ride the woman to unlimited ecstasy to build up orgasm before climaxing.

• **The straddle sex position**

The straddle sex position is a satisfying sex position for beginners and it is so great because it doesn't require a lot of efforts, so beginners can start their experimentation with this sex position to get the immense pleasure from their sex session as the dream about. Straddle sex position offers optimum sexual stimulation and body numbing orgasm and it works right for both partners. This sex position will have the man sit first on a surface or a comfortable chair and the woman sit facing the man and straddling him. Instead of the woman bouncing up and down, she will rather swirl herself around and then, rock back and forth so that the man penis hits the wall of her G-spot over and over again, The man can grab the woman breast from that angle to suck and draw the woman booty forward for deep penetration. The woman can help more up more sensations and thrills by leaning back for easier access to the clitoris as she keeps grinding the man still the explode.

• **Modified Doggy sex position**

This is a sex position that first time users will enjoy and have the orgasmic thrills throughout the duration of the sex making. It helps the partners pleasures themselves and rediscover all the zones that will makes them scream and moans in ecstasy. The modified doggy position would be a really adventurous sex position for the beginners to get freaky and crazy while getting it good on their genitals and other erogenous zones of their body. This is one sex position that will offer both partners back- arching and toe curling pleasure in no little way especially as the man get a good view of the woman's butt and clit. This sex position has the woman kneeling and bending in front of the man with her hands on the floor too. The man kneels behind her but in an upright position. A sex toy like the vibrator can be used to start off the sizzling session with stimulating the woman clitoris and then the man penetrate her from there. The woman can respond by throwing her legs a bit open and moving with the rhythm of the man thrusts. This will build more orgasmic sensation as they both grind along to heighten it and then climax.

• The 69 sex position

Beginners will find this legendary sex position alluring and it really good for people that are just trying out a new sex position away from the missionary sex position they must have been used to as this sex position gives each partner the ability of attending to each private part. This is to say the man will attend to the woman and vice versa. Each partner will focus on making the other partner feel good while at the same time focusing too on how the other partner is making him or her feels. This sex position have the man being on top of the woman but his face facing the feet of the woman and places his mouth on the woman's genital /clitoris and perform a fully vertical cunnilingus or blowjob, after some time he switch it and let the woman be on top facing his feet to give a hard blowjob to the cock. The mouth can be given a break too by throwing in some sex toys like the masturbation sleeve, vibrator or butt plug. Spice up the session with dirty talks, fingerings and fondling.

CHAPTER 3:
10 G-SPOT STIMULATING SEX POSITIONS

For a sex position to feel amazing then it must be hitting the most sensual spots for both the man and woman and this is when we should believe the heat is on the G-spot and we are getting it right because intense pleasure and multiple orgasm is eminent. The truth is that there are sex positions that can easily stimulate this spot and help give unimaginable pleasures. So if you want to drive your partner crazy and hit the G-spot for more stimulation, then you need to check out these 10 sultry sex positions that will help you achieve your aim.

• **The wheelbarrow sex position**

The wheelbarrow sex position is one position that gets both partners screaming and moaning to the clouds. You can't get it wrong with this naughty sex position when you are trying to hit on the G-Spot for more erotic stimulation. This sex position brings horniness any time the partners think about sex. This is a hot and sizzling hot position to try out. This sex position is both pleasuring for the man and woman though it will enable the man hit the woman G-spot easily and in no time. The woman will kneel in front of the man and the man will be behind her and penetrate the woman from behind. Once the man is inside the woman, the woman will then grab the man's ankles as the man will now slowly lift himself to stand supporting the woman with the slightly bent lap. To add more erotic twist the woman should add a Lube to her clitoris and squeeze her pelvic muscles along with the thrusts for great session of sex passion.

• **Lotus blossom position**

Lotus sex position is an amazing G-spot stimulating sex position partners can employ to mesmerize one another in the bedroom. This sex position is sure to help give the partners spine tingling orgasm that both deserved. If you are thinking of a sex position you both can relish and will allow great access to G-spot stimulation then you need to try out the Lotus blossom sex position it will surely makes the woman squirts as many times as possible and the man having all the orgasmic thrills from an awesome sex session. This sex position starts with the man sitting down on his butt with his legs crossed while the woman will be fairly close in front of the man almost like the yoga pose and she will sit on the man's crotch facing him, the woman can hold on to the man tightly by wrapping her arms around his back and putting her leg around the man's back too, then she pulls the man more tightly into her vagina and the man hold her firmly too by putting his arm around her. To add more sensation and stimulation the man's hands at the back can be used for a massage and rub the clit while the woman can be grinding and rocking the cock and also dry humping. The man will be having a grinding motion until the two partners erupt in an uncontrollable ecstasy. The man can go harder to stimulate the woman more and hit the G-spot stronger. This will aid the breast bouncing more by the woman and this sight alone is erotic for more thrills for the man. The woman can reciprocate the rhythm by throwing her booty back and forth so that both can finally explode in multiple orgasms.

• **Hot half headstand**

If you are looking for the optimal G-spot stimulating G-spot sex position, then going with the hot half headstand will be the best bet. This is one sex position that both partners can enjoy great stimulations on the genitals and a great way of working through the kinks together. This sex position is very popular with erotic stimulations because it does direct and help partners readjust to a position that they will be able to hit their G-spot easily to get the immense pleasure needed. This position will have the woman bending in front of the man, the man kneels behind the woman to penetrate from that angle, and the man will fold forward touching the woman. The woman will then grab the man's ankles as she raises her legs to the man side for deep stimulation and easy accessibility of hitting her G-spot. If the partners can't hold longer at the position then they can fall back to the missionary position and for more stimulation a rabbit vibrator can be used for ultimate sensual experience.

• Carnal craving sex position

Carnal craving sex position is one sex position that gives partners total control over depth, angle, pace, speed and even the stimulation level during sex session and as such it will help the man get all the thrills that comes with the session while helping gets the woman G-spot well stimulated to the seventh heavens. Both partners will be sure of quenching their lusty desires with this sultry sex position as they explore their bodies and hit all the needed spots to arouse them. The partners begin this position by sitting and facing one another. Then the man grab the woman waist and under her butt and lift her towards himself and drop her on his laps. The woman will wrap her arms behind the man 's neck and her legs around the man's waist for additional support and the woman will help direct the man's cock into her vagina while the man will thrust away at a rhythmic pace. The man can heighten the pleasure by pressing the cock sometimes on the woman's clits.

• Octopus sex position

Octopus sex position is an erotic sex position that gives the man the advantage of lasting longer and also giving the woman the opportunity of getting highly stimulated so that the man can hit her G-spot easily. This sex position offers both partner spines tingling orgasm and out of breath ecstasy as they continue to explore one another body and hitting on all the sensual spots to explore in multiple orgasms. With this sex position the man sits on the floor and lean backwards slightly, he can placed his hands behind his back for support then spread his legs a bit to balance himself, then bend his legs slightly afterwards, The woman will stand over the man, with her feet on either side of the man's waist and slowly lower herself on the cock or just squat on your cock, she will direct the cock to her vagina, once the cock is inside her she then sit on your lap and slowly lean backward. She lift up her right leg and leave it at the man's left shoulder while lifting the left leg and keeping it on the man's right shoulders. The man now start thrusting in and out now and intermittently change angle so as to be able to stimulate the G-spot, The man can use his fingers to rub her clit and press his cock a bit on her clit. The man can make the woman let out all kind of moaning sounds by reaching forward to suck the woman's clit, then penetrate and thrust harder again till the both climaxed.

• Coital alignment technique{c a t}

Coital alignment technique is an awesome sex position that will be sexually fulfilling for both partners. This sex position enable the man hit directly on the woman's G-spot because this sex position aid change the alignment of the woman's pelvis allowing the man pubic bone to rub against the girl's clitoris hereby delivering heighten sexual excitement to both partners. This sex position will be great for a little shy and naïve partners as well as beginners that need some easy to maneuver sex positions that are a lot easy to use. CAT can help partners really get intimate with theirselves as they explore one another bodies. This sex position can be started in the missionary way; the woman will be on her back and the man will be on top of her between her legs. The man now pulls himself up toward the woman's heads that his pelvis is a bit higher up on the girl's body, so instead of the man thrusting in and out, he would rather do more of grinding against the woman's pelvis. For more intense pleasure and to stimulate the G-spot more the man can help the woman part her labia apart so that his body rubs directly against the woman's clitoris or better still keep a pillow under the girl's hips so as to get more accessible angle. Lastly, the man can use some lube on the girl's clitoris to create a very extra slippery sensation when it touched. With this position the partners are sure of satisfying theirselves perfectly.

• Devilish doggy

Devilish doggy is a perfect sex position for hitting on the G-spot; this sex position can be described as the revamp version of the classic cowgirl. It helps both partners discover all the sensual and erotic spots on their body which only brings heavenly pleasure. This sex position will always leave the partner asking for more as the pleasure one another. Devilish doggy is a classic sex position which the woman goes down all four (both on her hands and knees) while the man pleasure and stimulate her from behind. With this position, the rear entry of penetration create a perfect amount of friction for both partners and of course it helps the man get a deeper penetration to elicit more pleasurable sensation while stimulating and hitting the woman's G-spot. This sex position begins with the woman kneeling and keeping her hands on the floor, the man also kneel behind her upright and penetrate the lady while holding her waist for support. The man can now start thrusting, intermittently the woman will part her legs a little wider so that the man can access her clitoris and can now play with it using the penis. Later the woman can take over too, by the man laying over the edge of the bed and the woman will straddle over the man and stretching her hands towards the man's feet. This will give the man a better view of the woman's body; of course this sultry view will arouse the man even more. A sex toy can be introduce at this point to help stimulate the woman's G-spot even more too to build up orgasm for both partners before both erupt in a volcanic orgasm.

• Sideways straddle sex position

There's absolutely no way partners wouldn't find this sex position alluring because this sex position is actually made for fantastic grinding action whereby it will allow for pleasurable thrusting and easy access to stimulating the G-spot. This sex position makes the woman be in a better position of controlling the pace, direction and depth of penetration, so therefore this totally means pleasures and bliss for the woman because the man will be hitting her right while pleasuring himself too. This sex position is called the arousal position because it quite arousing for both the man and the woman. The woman will decide on the amount of pressure that can be exerted on her clitoris to heighten the pleasure for her. With this position the man lie on his back with his legs flat on the floor, the woman will then lower herself to her knees and use her hand to guide the man's penis inside her with each of her legs on each side of the man's leg, then from this position the girl rock and ride the penis forth and back, rubbing the clitoris also against the man's pubic area and upper thigh. To get intense sensation for the woman, the man can readjust the positioning of his leg by widening it apart or closely together depending on the one that's better and again can also try to lean back or forward to get the right position for immense pleasure for his self too. This is always a win win sex position because both will enjoy the position, though the woman may enjoy more.

• The bridge sex position

The bridge sex position is one sex position that will be loved by both partners, it does help the partners explore their bodies in a way that enable the man have deep stimulation of the woman's G-spot which would lead to helping them fulfill all the sexual fantasies that have been in their heads. The bridge sex position will give the man satisfactory penetration and a nice angle in which he can hit on the woman's G-spot effortlessly which give the woman the intense pleasure that will send her to the sexual clouds. With this sex positions the woman's clitoris will be easily expose either in the front or at the centre so that the man would be able to stroke it and excitedly reach down to stimulate it. Starting this position, the man sit up on his ankles with his knees spread wide, then the woman stay on her back and put her feet flat on the bed and arch her hips up a bit so that she is in a bridge position. The man penetrate her from this angle and then grab her hips and use them as leverage when, he is thrusting back and forth inside the woman. The man can change the angle of his crouch to be lower or higher at some point for more bliss, and the woman can reciprocates same by lowering or raising her hips to be on the same rhythm with the man. The man can further heighten the sensation by raising his self up to his knees and letting the woman wrap her legs around his torso or better still pull her legs up so that her ankles rest on his shoulders. Some spanking can be added to this for more sexual excitement.

• **Mastery sex position**

The mastery sex position is a fun and satisfying sex position that will make both partners be in sexual frenzy in the course of using this position. The mastery sex position offers intimacy and sexual satisfaction for both partners as they stimulate all the erogenous zones of one another body. This sex position allows ample body contact for the partners that will aid fingering and sucking of the woman's clitoris to sexual bliss. This amazing sex position can be done in your car or on the beach, so you might want to skip the bedroom to spice it up. The man sit on the side of the bed, sofa or wherever they like and place his feet on the floor, but his butt and thigh should be on the bed or flat surface, then the woman kneel down on his lap or squat on his lap then wrap her hands around his neck, then the man penetrate that way and start thrusting into the woman as she remain on top of him. The woman can rock and grind on him too. The man can ask the woman to lift herself up and down to the rhythm of his thrusts to heighten the sensation and put them both in a sexual frenzy. The man can let his thick cock press against her clit and toss her onto her knees before slamming her hard from behind to make her clitoris swells from enough stimulation. The orgasm the both will experience from this sex position will be explosive.

CHAPTER 4:
CRAZY SEX POSITIONS FOR GETTING MORE DARING AND FREAKY

If you have been using some very usual sex position a billion and one time and it is becoming more of a routine now but you need something more daring that can give you and your partner some crazy and overwhelming orgasm, then you don't need to resort to your go-to sex positions any more, you just have to whip out some very freaky and risky sex positions that will bring a rush of your adrenaline back. It is sometimes worthy to use some crazy, wild and maybe weird sex positions some days to making you and partner dripping some juices in the bedroom. There are tips you need to apply when you need to have riskier and freakier sex with your partner. so if you need to give your partner that toe curling, back arching and screaming orgasm that will make your partner like your raw and rough sex position and even become obsess with the sex positions then you really need to communicate with your partner, let your partner know what you need and enjoy and likewise same with you knowing hers as well.

If you love crazy sex positions then you should go for the sex positions that you both love and works for you both to achieve your aim, with crazy sex positions you just have to start slow, don't jump into crazier ones when you are yet to try the crazy ones out. Spanking with crazy sex positions go hand in hand some people find spanking incredibly hot and arousing, so you can experiment with it with your partner, you can add the following naughty bits like floggers, whips, paddle, canes or slappers for your spanking with your crazy sex position to get the freakier feeling ever. Crazy sex positions can be done in your car, at a good breathtaking spots like on a beach, top of a cliff or mountain or a place with incredible view or even in a party.

So if you need some riskier and freakier sex positions that will awaken your sexual prowess and that of your partner with no restraints, then you should try out these ten explosive sex positions daily and you will have the ultimate pleasure, sensation and multiple orgasms you have always craved for during sex.

• The X-rated sex position

This is one sex position that can make you and partner go crazy and wild during your steaming sex Session. This sex position will need the woman doing more of the work needed in this position because she has to slides her body up and down against her man. When it comes to the thrusting the woman might need to hold on to something for support especially if the man is in control of thrusting depth and pace. The good thing about this crazy position is that it gives the partners the needed control to experiment with different types of stimulation to see what pleases them both. The partners will love to get an A+ view of taking charge of their orgasm, so it will be great for the partners to add to the crazy position some x-rated noises and of course letting one another know how they feel. This sex position is done with the man should lying face up on the bed, the woman gets on top and let her back face the man. The woman can now lower herself onto the man's penis while extending her legs towards the man's shoulders and ultimately relaxing her torso onto the bed between the man's feet. Let both the legs of the woman and that of the man form an X-shape and the woman can now start to slide up and down. The man feet can be used by the woman for added thrusting leverage if that will be necessary. The man can be spanking the woman booty and one or two sex toys can be thrown in too.

• Spork sex position

The spork sex position is one sex position you can use if you need to have some crazy smoking sex session. This is a kind of side by side sex position one can use for rear entry vaginal sex or even for anal sex if one want it that way. Spork sex position can be done in most places it just about the partners being creative with it. Trying is out on a picnic blanket in the field or on the back of a car wouldn't be a bad idea. This wild sex position makes couples and partners have a good view of their bodies which will increase arousal and also have free hands to explore other erogenous zones for tingling sensation. Oral sex and double team stimulations can be added to this sex position. The man and woman will lie on their sides and the man will rest the front of his torso and groin against the woman's back and rear end. Then instead of leaving the leg straight the woman should draw her legs up against her chest like in a fetal position. The man can give the woman a good sucking of the clitoris here and a wet fingering too. Then the man can draw his legs up slightly to curve around the woman's waist and will finally wrap his arms around the woman torso and gently penetrate to start pumping in and out deeply. You can throw in some sex toys to heighten the sensation before finally exploding in orgasms

• Standing wheelbarrow sex position

This wild and crazy sex position might not be for the faint-hearted so if you are just starting out with some crazy sex position, you might need to think about this a bit before trying it out with your partner. This sex position can be liken to downward dog style but with deep thrusting and hitting hard on the G-spot, one may be able to stay in this sex position just for a little time. This sex position is a challenging one but it gives deep penetration and intense sensation. With this sex position the woman starts out on all fours {hands and knees on the floor}, maybe a pillow can be placed under her arms for comfort, the man kneels behind her and then grasp her ankles lifting them slightly off the ground while the woman's legs remain bent at the knees level, then the man can penetrate the woman while completely straightening his legs or maybe leaving slightly bent. The man need to balance his body and control the movement of it too. The man can make the woman moan loudly by pressing the cock on her clit and using the rabbit vibrator too, the moans and screams can drive the man crazy to enjoy the sex better.

• **Swiss ball blitz**

This is a weirder and crazier sex position but fun sex position; this sex

position is about using a stability ball. This will need the both partners to balance on the workout ball. The man can be on top of the ball to master control and depth, which can aid the movements to be faster and deeper which comes from the extra buoyancy from the exercise ball. To get into this position the man sits on the ball with his feet on the floor, the woman joins him but faces away from the man, she will backs the man and sits on the man, the man can now penetrate the woman from the angle of entry by arching the behind and pressing further into the groin, then the woman can turn forward to stimulate the base of the man's penis, the perineum and the scrotum while the man can as well reach out to stimulate the woman's nipples and clitoris too. If you love some sexual fetish like biting and scratching you can introduce it too with this sex position to add more pleasure and build up orgasms. Then the man can penetrate the woman either through vagina or have anal sex to have orgasmic thrills before climaxing.

• Table top sex position

This is one raunchy sex position that puts both partners at the same level especially for partners of different height; this crazy position can be very good for a very hot sexy session. Aaron opined that this position really provides some serious leverage for thrusting and help the partners go really crazy with pleasure and sensation. One can really get rough and raw with this sex position with some sex fetishes like choking, spanking, scratching etc. This sex position can be done in the most creative way, it could be on the bed, kitchen counter or it could be any clean surface you can come across at that moment. The woman should get on the surface lying down, she then brings her knees together upward and then twist to one side, and then the man can enter the woman from this position. To get the a heightened pleasure the woman can be in control of the movement too, by directing her butt to the rhythm of the thrusting and the man thrust back and forth in all directions to really get the woman G-spot. To build strong orgasmic sensation, the man can intermittently use a dildo or erotic furniture to make the pleasure more intense.

• Pretzel sex position

Pretezel sex position is one of the slightly weird but really enjoyable sex positions that is surprisingly easy to use but great if you need some unusual sex position. This position enables powerful thrusts but at the sideways angles that will feel different, steamy and hot. So if you need the deep penetration just like doggy style but a bit harder with all eye contact then you need to try out this style. The woman lie on her back, while the man kneel down in front of the woman and lift the woman right and left leg so that it can curl around the man's waist. The man can start with oral sex before going anal and then penetrate the vagina with this sex position and then some spanking can be done with some sex tools like the slapper, flogger or paddle. With this sex position the hands will be free; the hands can work on other erotic zones of the body to heighten the pleasure that is needed. Stimulating the nipples, penis, scrotum and cervix for more moans and screams.

• The spider sex position

This is a crazy sex position that will enable partners using it to wiggle, grind and gyrate their butts away any how they like it. This style will be very comfortable and relaxing for the partners especially for the woman. According sex therapist Martilda Nouh, she described this sex position as a tease though it still a very challenging one. The good thing about this position is the fact that the movement can be controlled by the partners which enable them to rock forth and back to get into a satisfying rhythm and deep penetration for more arousal. This position will have both the man and woman facing each other at first on a seated position for foreplay like lots of kissing, dry humping, fingering, stimulations, sucking etc, then the woman can lie back and the man scoots in between the woman's legs to achieve penetration, then the man can now follow suit by lying back too but still maintain the erection inside the woman. For the partners to get this right each of the couple lie flat on their back with their head in between the other legs and buttocks touching. Then to get the possibility of greater movement the partners need to bring both knees up so that they both have something to grip during the motions and the man can continue to pump away.

• The golden arch sex position

Golden arch sex position is a crazy sex position that would afford partners the privilege of viewing each other full bodies. This sex position gives partners the absolute control over the speed, depth and angle of the thrusts. Sex guru Annabelle K night revealed that the golden arch sex position is perfect for learners and professionals alike in the game of practicing crazy sex positions. This sex position gives both man and woman better orgasms. This sex position helps those that really need more G-spot stimulation. to achieve this position the man sit with his legs straight and the woman sits on top of him with her knees bent over his thighs, the woman will then lean backward so that she can get the cock well in her vagina to enjoy more sensation, the woman can do the grinding by lifting her ankles, she can still lean back further for more G-spot stimulation and as she can access her clitoris for more stimulation. To get freakier with this position a vibrator or a bullet vibes, should be used on the clitoris as well, and while the man goes on a shallow penetration for that moment. Some spanking with a whip will come in handy here for a pain-sweet sensation that sparks sensual flames all over the body.

• David copperfield sex position

David cooperfield sex position is a freaky sex position which will leave both partners screaming in ecstasy because the result achieved here is beyond wild and crazy and this sex position works so well with performing oral on a partner. Sex experts are of the view that this sex position needs the woman to be strong enough to hold herself up on her arms because the man needs to grab her leg and wraps them around his waist and the man will be giving thrusting in an ascending stroking motion. This will creates a tighter experience for both partner therefore being an added advantage for them .This sex position is about the both partners getting the ultimate banging experience. The woman goes down on her stomach with placing a pillow under her pelvis and lifting up her butt while placing her arms down for support and the man will go down on the woman from behind to give her some oral stimulation and dry humping away. To get more sensation the woman can lift her legs and place them on the man's shoulders too for more access to her G-spot. O'Reilly says one can dry hump the woman by stimulating her Mons pubic, this stimulation will help to rev up the woman for further sex sensation and makes her juice dripping and afterwards the man can now penetrate her from this angle to hit on the G-spot which will send sensations to the both partners. Easy orgasm is sure for both the man and woman with this position.

• **The grinder sex position**

The grinder sex position is one hell of a crazy sex position that can engulf users with immense pleasure and drive them wild and crazy on one another. Anyway one must be careful with this freaky sex position, since penetration might need to come from the rear but it still an amazing sex position since it a tight fit for both the male and the female, so it will give both partners the control of their movement and the opportunity of them getting their rear view. Of course this needs the woman leg to be lifted a bit and this will definitely helped the man to ultimately stimulate the clit which will heighten the pleasure for the woman. It will be a win- win situation for the partners when once they are naturally able to master the art of this position. The man should lie with one of his knee bent, the woman be on top with face away, she will straddle her thigh and lower herself on the penis to grind away. The woman can adjust while grinding away so that she will be able to hit her G-spot. This sex position also allows other form of sex like oral or anal depending on what the partners want, there can be a bit of spanking too, you can as well throw in some sex toys that will help with more sweetness. Emilia Bach, a sex therapist gave her personal view about this sex position, she opined that this sex position is really freaky and crazily harmless but can hit one's G-spot all the time.

CHAPTER 5:
ADVANCED SEX POSITIONS FOR BETTER STIMULATIONS AND STRONGER ORGASM

Most things we need to achieve in life need to be on repeat to get better and same is applicable in having a better stimulation and stronger orgasms. Partners need to explore and exploit more with sex positions to know which sex positions will work wonders for them. The hottest spark in one's sexual life needs some new sex positions to stroke the flames to fire. Every now and then one needs to ease off the sex drought that is almost engulfing one's sex life and bedmatics skills. The good news is that anytime you introduce something raunchy and frenzy into your bedroom then you are setting yourself up for a more stimulating and sensual experience. According to Vanessa Marin, a licensed sex therapist in Los Angeles area opined that our brain craves newness all the time because the brain is so much involved with excitement and fulfillment. One of the best way to know which sex position can give you immense stimulation and orgasms is to explore and experiment with different positions, so that the areas that your old positions couldn't Stimulate will be stimulated and you can convincingly choose the one that will give you the best desire. Below are the convincing and goal oriented sex positions that can effortlessly gives partners better stimulation and stronger orgasm. These sex positions will help partners to always be in the mood for intense orgasmic sex. So follow this step by step sex positions technique and get stronger stimulation and orgasm out of your sizzling sex sessions.

• Corkscrew sex position

This is a deep penetration sex position for perfect ecstasy which put both partners in direct contact, this can be done slowly if need be and the body can be left to relax while using this sex position. For the woman this position needs some agility and flexibility from her. So basically the corkscrew can be viewed as one of the porn sex positions that can be seen almost everywhere online and it will be so much fun for the woman because it opens the woman up for full, deep exposure which can be a little animalistic. There is something alluring and delicious about the corkscrew sex position. The man will be on his knees and will grab the woman from an angle facing away from him, the woman would place her right leg on top of man's hip hereby opening her body up while her other leg remains relax at the knees, the woman would then grabs the man's back from the side while the man enters the woman slowly to hit directly on the G-spot to start pumping in and out and the woman will respond too, to get the rhythm moving. The woman just has to be agile with her right arm grabbing unto the man's back to hold on tight. Keeping her legs tight to enable a tighter hold on the man as he thrusts, the woman too will be thrusting her hips slightly to the tempo, with all of this, the sensation will be over the top which will give both partners memorable stimulation and multiple orgasm. This sex position is tested and trusted.

• Leap frog sex position

Leapfrog sex position is a top sex position for G-spot stimulation, the leap frog sex position help to change the angle of entry for the vagina, it also shorten it making penetration out rightly deeper and delicious. So if partners want the most pleasurable orgasm filled sex life with an easy to do sex position then using leapfrog sex position will be the answer. Though sex experts are of the view that this position can lead air to be sucked into the vagina but this is totally harmless though it may cause unusual noise but not to worry, the noise might bring more arousal after all. This sex position have the woman getting on her hands and knees, then keep her hips raised, the head and arms can be rested on the bed and the man can enter through the rear for deeper penetration, maybe the woman can use the pillow as well by resting on it, the man can use his hands to stimulate the woman clitoris for immense pleasure before introducing a dildo to build up orgasmic sensation before penetrating the woman again. With this sex position the pleasurable effect can heighten more if the woman leans forward to help adjust the movement of the thrusting. This synchronization by the two bodies will absolutely elicit unlimited pleasure and multiple orgasms.

• **Cowgirl's helper sex position**

Rebecca Rosenblat , a sex therapist and the author of seducing your man specifically recommends this sex position for partners that really need deep penetrations and multiple orgasm, it is one sex position that will be less stressful on the legs and making climaxing a lot more easier. This sex position gives the woman a dominant advantage which helps to delay the man climaxing before the woman, so it becomes a win-win situation for both sexes. Cowgirl's helper sex position is almost like the popular cowgirl sex position but this one is more appropriate for deep thrusting and for maximum orgasm. So with cowgirl's helper sex position, the perks of it is that there will be great view of their bodies by the partners and the woman will get the chance to get more stimulations for her actions, this will afford the woman some very great G-spot stimulation and going so deep as she want with each thrusts will be totally her prerogative. Just like the cowgirl sex position, with this too, the woman will on top pushing off the man as the man lies on his back. The difference here is that the man will assist with his hands by holding the woman thigh or hips which will enable him support her weight so as to be easy for the man to rise and meet the woman's every thrusts. To get the best from this sex position is to alternate between shallow and deep thrusting to stimulate the different parts of the vagina which will aid hard stimulation and makes both explode in ecstasy and subsequent bouts of orgasm. The man need to be agile with this sex position because he needs to be at the same thrusting level with the woman too.

• **Cowboy sex position**

As the name implies, this sex position fit more for the man than the woman but both partners benefit immensely from the sex position for both deep penetration and multiple orgasm. The cowboy sex position is almost like the cow girl sex position only that this one has the man being on top of the woman unlike the cowgirl position. The woman in this position wouldn't have to do much since the man will be the one riding but for deeper penetration and stimulation the woman can intermittently spread her legs wider and lifts her hips upwards to bring the vagina closer to the penis. The man using this sex position will do all the thrusting and might have to change the angle of entry sometimes if the entry he is using isn't enabling deep thrusting as anticipated. This sex position will be ultimate for partners that will need deep penetration and making the woman have all the wetness for easy entry which will bring unlimited pleasure and hotness hereby making them explodes in sexual excitement as desired. With cowboy sex position the woman lie on her back while the man is on top, to straddles her. The man will inserts his penis gently through the tight opening created by the woman's semi-closed legs. This tightness is to help increase the intensity of the penetration and stimulation so that the both get the amount of pleasure and thrills that comes with this position and of course the stronger orgasm that was needed in the first place. To even get it hotter the man can also fondle with the woman's breast and gently hold down the woman's wrists for more bondage action.

• **Ballet dancer sex position**

This is a must used sex position for great stimulation and stronger orgasm says Dr Yvonne K. Fulbright Ballet dancer sex position affords the partners more fun time with stimulation of the pleasurable zones and makes them climax during the course of the steamy sex session again and again, apart from that, this sex position always offers the partners quality face time which will make them look into each other dreamy eyes to get all the sexual satisfaction and connections. This sex position at the end of it leaves the couple drained and laying still in one another's arms for soothing effects. Ballet dancer sex position needs the woman standing and facing the man, then the man will lift one foot and hook it around the woman's waist and can penetrate the woman from that position, it will be more alluring if both partners are of same height since it is an intimate face to face position. To get more stimulation and stronger orgasm the woman should go down to suck the man's cock while the man bends over to finger the woman. Thereafter they can go back to the sex position but this time the woman should raise her leg a bit higher for even deeper penetration which will aid explosive pleasure and ecstasy as thrusting that way will be so smooth and unhindered.

• **Magic mountain sex position**

Magic mountain sex position is one of the hottest sex positions that allows for deep penetration hereby making one to hit the G-spot easily and stimulate the clitoris to higher heavens and bring forth to the partners or couples multiple orgasms. Partners that need deeper stimulation can't go wrong using the magic mountain because as the name implies it works like magic by sending electrifying sensation throughout the body during the sex session. The pleasure and bliss one derive from using this sex position can't be overemphasized. With this sex position the man hands is so free and that could be used to explore all the erogenous zones of the woman's body to elicit more stimulation and excitement. The man sits and bends his legs, leaning back on his forearms and hands. The woman does same but will need to inch toward the man until they both have a contact. This enable the partners really get connected from looking at one another. Then the stimulation can be increased at this point through the woman grinding her clitoris more against the man's pelvis, the stimulus can be hotter if some slide ice cubes are let on the man's chest to allow the cold water collect at the base of the pelvis. Better still the man bends over the woman so that the woman back is against his chest, so that the closeness will allow the stimulation to be intense for better climax.

• Tap dance sex position

As the name implies this is a sex position that involves more tapping than rubbing of the clitoris and can readily cause quick and intense sensations for those who find direct stimulation too intense or overwhelming. This sex position has an unmatched stimulation potential. This erotic position will gives the couples especially the woman illusive feelings about the sex position for a while. This sex position will help add more steam to the sex session. To even make the tapping hotter and harder, then the man should help in the tapping in the faster and harder way to create different sensation all over the body. The woman should lie on one side of the body with one of her leg extended or straight while the other is bent, using one hand then she gently separate and hold the labia to the sides and gently apply a drop of lube to the exposed clitoris, the man lie on his side facing the woman begin tapping the clitoris gently to cause intense pleasure before thinking about penetrations. The essence of this sex position is to cause deeper stimulation and stronger orgasm as the partners roll in the hay.

• Lap dance sex position

This is a sex position that will give both man and the woman various orgasmic sensations. Both partners get to thrill one another in this position. The lap dance enable the woman to make sex visually appealing to the man, hereby stimulating all this sexual senses and putting him under intense pleasure that will give the man toe-curling, back arching and screaming orgasm that will help keep the man sexually obsessed with the woman. This sex position can really work with anal sex; the man can supercharge the woman pleasurable zone by massaging the clitoris with his fingers. This sex position will give the users the deeper stimulation and stronger orgasm they both need. Using a tall backed chair or a desk and padded with some pillows, the man sits on it. The woman will then straddle the man's penis and lean back slightly and also place her hands on his knees. The woman will extend her legs with one at a time until each of her angle rest on the man's corresponding shoulders. The woman can then pump her booty back and forth at a speed that will make her moan. For the woman to supercharge her thrusting power she should balance her weight between her hands and ankles. The woman will remain on top grinding on the man while the man penis stays deep inside her and this help provide fantastic G-spot stimulation. The man can help the woman bounce up and down on him by using his arms for support.

• Upstanding citizen sex position

Upstanding citizen sex position is a must try for partners that needs that deeper stimulation and explosion of orgasm because this is sex position for a very steamy romance session. April Masini , author of think and date like a man recommends this sex position for partners and couples that need to upped their erotic stimulation during sex session. This raunchy sex position give the woman especially great stimulation that would be memorable for a very long time. This position wouldn't be uncomfortable for the man because he will have to spreads his thighs slightly and not lock his knees which make him more relaxed. The woman will first straddle the man by wrapping her legs around the man's body; the man will stand erect and support the woman in his arms and penetrate the woman on his feet. This sex position can start from the bed anyway and have the man picking the woman up from the bed without disrupting the flow of things that were alright on gear but if the woman is agile enough she can hop on the man from standing position. To get the stimulation intense the man can push the woman up a wall gently and in a careful manner. The man should endeavor to keep his knees unlocked and thighs spread slightly though. The woman can supercharge his partner by moaning out when the sensation is intense, to also put the man in a sexual frenzy too, which will enable them to have not just a screaming orgasm but multiple ones that will last on their minds for a long time.

CHAPTER 6:
TOP 10 SEX POSITIONS FOR DEEP CONNECTIONS AND SEXIER LOVE MAKING

You just have to mesmerize your partner with mind blowing sex to really keep them and have deep bonding with them. Just a quickie in the bathtub or some dry kisses before rolling over will not cut it. You need to satisfy your partner in some well planned steamy sex session that will leave them always horny anytime they are around you, in fact they can't literally get their hands off you. Having a bomb ass sex with your partner will make you the woman feeling sexier while the man will have deep connection with you. it is good to make sex a lot more fun that will drive your partner crazy, use sultry sex positions that will make them explode in ecstasy and will help remind him or her always why you are in a relationship with your them

It is pertinent you turn to sex positions that will strengthen or build the deep connection you need with your partner. .whether you are trying to rekindle the flames of a real love or trying to foster a more profound link with someone new, you need to try out the below hot sex positions that will enable you both to always be in the mood for intense orgasmic sex session filled with fire and deep connection. This will aid your partner fall in love with you all over again.

• **Side by side position**

You can get your love flames burning very high for deep connection using this sex position. This sex position will leave you both grasping for breathe after the hot sex session and it will foster deep connection because of eye contact and physical closeness it afford the partners during the sex session. With this sizzling position you and your partner will be delving into a new world of pleasure because the position offers the man opportunity to get explicit access to your woman's G-spot while pleasuring himself too. This position also promotes deep bonding and make the woman sexier through the eyes gazing by the partners, kissing is done effortlessly, and there is ease of communication too since the partners can see one another's responses to stimulation. This sex position begins with the man and woman lying side by side by each other; the man draped his leg over the woman's hip so that he can pull the woman's vagina deeper into him. The woman can sometimes have her knees bent up to her breasts for a deeper penetration. To heighten the sexual heat the man should asked the woman to part her thigh a bit, the man would then use his cock to rub her clitoris and allow her scream in excitement for a while before penetrating deeply and thrusting forth and back again still the both climax.

• **Spooning position**

This is a perfect sex position that will make partners scream off their lungs in ecstasy as the pleasure one another, this position is both a sexual position and a cuddling technique, so one can imagine the orgasmic thrills partners will enjoy when using this hot sex position. This sex position will leave the woman feeling sexier and having a strong connection with her partner. The position is a rear entry position which is like the doggy style position and it is ideal for partners that need a deeper and more pleasurable sensation, it a great position since it allows partners work through the action of sex together. Spooning sex position put less strain on the muscles which makes the couple last for long while making love. This sex position has the man lying on his side while the woman lies in front of the man facing away, so this means that the woman will be in the inner spoon position while the man will be in the outer spoon position preparing for the entry penetration. The man enters her from behind; the man can add more sensation by grabbing and fondling with her breast from behind, stimulating her clitoris and finally going anal with her before climaxing.

• Doggy style

A psychosexual therapist based in Palo Alto, California, said that this sex position gives partners orgasmic thrills especially the women deep penetration that leads to immense pleasure and can help the partner have some deep connection after the steamy sex session. So if you need a sex position that will give your partner the adrenaline rush and keep sexual flames burning in the relationship while also keeping you the woman sexier and create deep connection for you both in the relationship, then using the doggy style will just be it. The doggy sex position is pretty easy the woman lies on her stomach with her butt in the air, maybe with a pillow under her pelvis for extra support, the man stands behind her to penetrate from behind but before then he can stimulate the clitoris to bliss with a vibrator. The man can make the woman scream more by introducing anal sex and cap it up with vagina sex but must apply plenty of lube and continue deep thrusting still the both erupt in multiple orgasms.

• The chair sex position

You can't get it wrong with this naughty sex position especially when it comes to sex making that will create deep bonding because of the close body contact involved with this position. The position gets the man all excited since he will be the one sitting and taking in all erotic view of the entire woman's body. The woman on the other hand who is on top of the man will be having it easier with the stimulation of her clitoral and G-spot with this position. The good thing about this position is that it enable the partners find the right spots to stimulate and the intensity and speed can build up from there. The position will help the partners ditch the bed for a chair so using the chair than a bed will add some zing to the already sizzling sex position. So you can check out the chair position because it will not only add romp to your sex session but foster deep connection and intimacy with your partner. This sex position start with the man sitting upright on the chair and the woman sitting on the man but backing him, The man can start with foreplay like fondling, fingering and stimulating the clitoris and massaging each other bodies, then the woman gently now direct the erect cock to her vagina and lean forward so that she can have the ease of deep penetration while moving her hips up and down in circles which could be backward or forward. To heighten the sexual pleasure the woman can turn around to stimulate all the erogenous zones with her hands and mouth and this will help put fire on both bodies, drawing you both together to create a better connection that can't be denied. The man can take over now and ride the woman to stupor with some deep thrusting.

• **Woman on top sex position**

Woman on top sex position is a build up on the missionary sex position where the woman is on top. This sex position is classic for partners that really want to connect emotionally with one another through good sex. Apart from the hot sex romp this sex position offers partners it also offers deep connection through direct eye contact, sexy sounds and sensual touches and there is much more control of deep penetration too with this sex position. This sex position according to Zoldbrod will help the woman on top have clitoral stimulation which will make her reach multiple orgasms in the course of the sex session. This sex position can be started with the man lying on his back while the woman is comfortably on top, the woman grab the man's penis and give it a huge blowjob to stretch the erection and to build up sensation before directing it to her vagina to insert, the woman leans her body forward and her hand beside or on the man head on the bed for support. The woman will then use her hips to rock back and forth or side by side till she can find the angle that let her rub her clitoris against the man's lower abdomen or pubic bone. This will make the man be practically caged inside the woman as she brings herself almost to climax. She can also engage the man's view by throwing her booty in his face while riding him hard forth and back. The man can be spanking the woman butt and responding to the rhythm of the ride still the both climax.

• The lotus sex position

The lotus sex position is called the deep connection sex position because it provides face to face intimacy that can boost deep connection with a partner while making love. This sex position elicit excitement and erotic feelings, with this sex position the bodies are touching entirely and the partner's faces are close enough to have some fun together, there's intense eye contact , whispers, naughty talks and kisses are sure to follow with this sex position. If you need to feel sexier and have deep connection with your partner then you need to try out the lotus sex position, you will sure have all that you had needed. Start this sex position with the woman sitting with her legs loosely crossed, while the man sit on top of the woman facing her and with his legs wrapped around the woman's back. The man penetrate the woman that way and focus now on moving up and down with slow sensual movement to build sexual thrills gradually. The woman can as well be grinding and rocking to the man rhythm, to build more orgasmic sensation the woman should put her arms under the man's arm and reach to grab his shoulders; this will make room for the woman to pull herself up and down on the man while intensely grinding and rocking him. There should be intermittent kissing, smooching, fondling, naughty talks etc in between. The man can heighten the pleasure to achieve back-arching, toe curling screaming orgasm by thrusting and grinding deeply.

• Hold me sex position

Hold me sex position can give partner spine tingling pleasure while facilitating emotional intimacy and deep connection. This sex position will always leave the partner asking for more as the pleasure one another and also help to build deepest connection because this sex position offers the opportunity of partners having eye contact, caressing and kissing themselves during the course of this sensational sex session. Hold me sex position can be done anywhere so you can skip the bedroom and your usual routine with this sex position. This sex position will need the man standing upright and the woman first going on her knees to give the man a good suck on his cock, then she now jump on the man and the man need to hold the woman into his arms and the woman should wrap her legs around the man's waist and her arms should be around his neck. This is a typical sex position to promote body contact and connection as the partners come face to face with one another. Before penetrating the woman, the man can finger and stimulate her clit, kiss and suck away, then penetrate the woman now and grab her booty and push it forward so that he can have deep penetration. The woman can as well respond to the rhythm by pushing herself forth and back and to heighten the pleasure the man can place the woman's back against a wall for support and then thrust deeply till the both explode in multiple orgasms.

• Hands free sex position

This is one sex position that apart from setting partners bodies on fire also connects them passionately when used. The outstanding feature of this sex position is that the sex position enables the partner's hands to be free for more arousal touches. Making love and have good amount of fingering and erotic touches help ignite swirling sexual feelings and this can bring about massive excitement and thrills for the partners, such that a remembrance of love making by the partner is fascinating and this will help keep them very close and deep into one another. This sex position promotes face to face contact for the partners which will enable them smile at one another while also having very close eye contact too. Sex position of this nature can make partners be very emotional and want to always be in another arm. This sex have the man sit on a chair while the woman is astride facing him{ that is her legs wide apart on each side of the man's leg} and the woman feet should be on the floor. This position will enable the man to face the woman, same with the woman too. With them facing one another they can begin the love making with foreplay, like the man giving the woman some tantalizing kisses, whispers into her ears, cuddle, fondle with the breast before penetrating. If the woman needs more intense pleasure she can be lifting her butt a bit higher while the man is thrusting and this can also help the man to have a deeper thrusting. The free hands they have because of this sex position can be used to rub, tingle and finger other erogenous spots of the body. The whole body feels thrilling sensation and the climax will be heavenly.

- **Snow angel sex position**

If you are looking for a smooth transition sex position away from your comfort sex style that will give mind-blowing orgasm, then this sex position will be perfect for you and your partner. This sex position would not only bring deep connections but will get your partner moaning and screaming in uncontrollable ecstasy. It is one sex position that hitting the G-spot is made easy and easily accessible as well as the man pleasuring himself to stupor. It just needs the woman to be flexible and agile to get this position right. This sex position have the woman lying on her back while the man is on top her, the woman then draw her thighs into the man chest and goes further to place her legs over her shoulders. This position will allow the man brings the woman pelvis off the mattress, so that the tilt of the woman hips will allow the man penetrate deeply into her with this position the man will have undeniable access to the woman G-spot. Rock the woman forth and back until the both climax with a bang.

• Missionary sex position

If you are looking for a sex position that will offer sexiness and deep connection in the bedroom then you should try out this good old sex position. No matter how old a trick may be being creative with it will suffice. This is applicable too to this sex position you just have to use the creative angle that is written on this book. This sex position is perfect for boosting deep connection during lovemaking. From a personal view, this position allows the partners to be able to kiss, lock fingers together, and the proximity allows for some erotic talks that would arouse the partners even more. There is more connectedness with this position because partners will be wrapped in each other's arms, leg intertwined and a lot of eye contact and this will make the partners sexier, and lovemaking will be sweeter. This position can be called a man on top or couple facing each other. While the woman is on her back, the man climbs on top and penetrate the woman from there as in the right old fashioned way. You can add a rabbit vibrator to the mix to get the woman screaming and moaning away. The man can finger the woman's clitoris too to heighten the pleasure, then insert his penis again and thrust deeply until they both come in multiple orgasm..

CHAPTER 7:
PRACTICABLE SEX POSITIONS THAT CAN HELP PARTNERS LAST LONGER IN BED

We all give out the vibes that we desire good sex just like the oxygen the breath, in as much as we desire sex positions that will give us spine tingling, back toe- curling, back arching and mind-blowing orgasm but it can be frustrating if this literally happens in a split second when all we needed was a sex session that is so passionate and we can relish for a long while. Because it worth every bit to satisfied our partners sexually then we should be ready to recharge, revive and reload our naughty bits so as to keep our partners spell-bound in the bedroom which will help them last longer and always feel horny anytime they are with us.

The sure way to make partners last longer on bed is just to change the sex position repertoire. Slow and steady naughty sex positions can be of immense help here. Sex position that will make partners take a breather and readjust their pace can be introduced while partners unleash their wild side and tap into each other animalistic urges and really blow off the sexual steam. Below are 10 tantalizing and sizzling sex positions that you can use to overwhelm your partner with intense pleasure while having it subtle and slow to have a longer sex session together.

• The lap dance sex position

This raunchy sex position can get any man to the clouds with intense pleasure, whether it by sucking or rubbing the tip of the cock before allowing him to penetrate, but it sure going to be shallow penetration so that both will not be over stimulated to get to orgasm very fast. The partners are sure going to give each other some orgasmic thrilling to get them going steadily before climaxing. This is one sex position that the man will relax and enjoy the stimulation from the woman even as the woman makes herself more visually appealing by pressing her boobs on his chest while giving him a massage on the scrotum. With this sex position the man sit first on a surface with his leg wide open while the woman will be on her feet backing the man, then she will gently lower yourself and grab his penis and guide it into her vagina, then grind slowly on your man, then, she can intermittently increase the intensity by bouncing her booty up and down to give him some real pleasure, she can as well bend forwards or backward to get the full length of the erected penis right inside her. At the same time the woman can look over her shoulder and make eye contact and kiss the man, she should continue with slow and subtle grinding which will enable them last longer before they both let out screaming orgasms.

• The valedictorian sex position

The valedictictorian sex position is a very seductive sex position that can elicit overtly strong excitement for partners that uses it, this sex position involves slow grinding that will pleasure both partners and makes them go weak in the knee in respond to all the naughty things they are slowly doing to their body. Like the thrills is killing them softly. Oral sex can be used with this sex position to put the partners in a euphoria that will get them to the seventh heaven. With The valedictorian sex position the woman lie on her back while your man is on top just like the missionary sex position but this time around the woman will raise his two legs up and extend them straight out to form a v shape, this will allow the cock to have a shallow contact with the vulva so as to have slow thrusting from the man so as to enable the man remain in the woman for a long time. To heighten the sensation the woman can use her hands to give the man a massage and intermittently suck the penis before directing it back to her vagina. The man can then ride the woman to stupor while the woman holds his waist as the climax together.

• **The cross sex position**

The cross sex position is a suggestive sex position to pump pleasure into the entire sensual parts of each partner's body. This sex position can make the partner's adrenaline level pump up as fast as possible, because the pleasure that will engulf them will be uncontrollable with this sex position. The penetration with this sex position will be deeper but at controllably rate and each thrust will come with its sensation that will stupefy partners and make them come with an earth quaking screams. To achieve this the man lies on his side facing the woman, while the woman lie on her back perpendicular to the man's body with her leg draped over the side of the man's pelvis, the woman press her crotch up against the man's own and she open her legs so that the man can penetrate easily. The man penetrates from that angle moving back and forth and holding onto the woman's thighs for leverage. The woman can also respond to the motion by pushing herself closer to get each thrust as the man slowly thrusts away. While the free hands move up and down on the sensual parts of the body. The woman can let the man have a good view of her clitoris by parting her labia a bit wide to drive him sexually crazy ,the woman can also work her waist to the rhythm of the man's thrust, to give him that toe- curling feelings. The woman should keep the penis tight in her throughout each thrusting still they explode in multiple orgasms.

• The flatiron sex position

Partners wanting to last longer during sex can't go wrong using this unique sex position. This sex position offers long lasting pleasure as the partners subtly rock themselves to unforgettable ecstasy. flatiron sex position allow the partners to take a break and reconnect again so that they will enjoyed themselves and still be sexually active for a good duration of time. A lot of couples will love this sex position, not with the position allowing the man's cock to fill up the woman's vagina and tightly glued to the vagina because of this position. This sizzling hot position enable lot of spanking and stimulation of the partners' erogenous zones that will help heighten the pleasure they will receive. Flatiron sex positions have the woman lying on her stomach on the bed in a plank position while the man straddles her. The woman raises her hips towards the man to allow for deeper penetration because the tighter the penis in the woman, the more sensation the couples will feel. So instead of the man to be fast and pounding he will go slowly but grinding deeply for good amount of sensation. The man will intermittently change from oral sex to vagina sex to give room for lasting effects. So partners that need to last longer during sex should try out this sex position and the woman shouldn't forget to lift her hip intermittently to help keep the penis in her for a long time.

• Butterfly

Couples that use this sex position are sure to last longer during any steamy sex session. This sex position would not just make couples last longer in bed but get the woman dripping wet and making the partners go crazy with multiple orgasms. If couples need to get mind-blowing and spine tingling pleasure then this sex position is sure to provide all of that. Butterfly sex position offers visual appeal because every inch of the body will be on display and of course this is an erotic way of evoking sexual bliss. With butterfly sex position partners are sure to be overwhelmed in ecstasy as they ride and do other naughty things to the body. The woman will lie on her back while the man stands or kneels next to the woman to enter from that angle but before penetration, foreplay can be started with the woman sitting on the man face to take oral sex and the man can be touching the woman mound to create more sexual tension. One or two sexual toys can be thrown in to the mix, this will create more frenzy and the woman body will be ready to penetrated, the woman can go back to the former position while the man penetrate her while she holds his waist for support, The woman should move her own waist with the man rhythm and let out some moans to get the man crazy. The man goes grinding in circular form to keep the steady and slow tempo for a long lasting effect. The woman can also give him oral sex by sucking his cock and directing the penis back to her juice dripping vagina, the man continues with the thrusting while woman touches the man other kiss-ass erogenous zones still both of them erupt in uncontrollable orgasm.

• **The sitting sex position**

This is another sex position that will help rock couple's sexual world in no hold barred manner. This sex position is a sweet and sensual one can make couple's screw off their head, because this sex position gives a perfect intense pleasure that is unimaginable. So if you need a sex position that will help you and your partner last longer during sex, the sitting sex position is what you need to try out. It is one sex position couples might take some breaks without killing the active sexual activity going on till they both erupt in multiple orgasmic thrills that will leave them both drained. Performing this sex position start with the man sitting down upright on his butt, the woman goes down first to elongate the erection of the penis by sucking it, then she slowly lower herself on the man by sitting and facing him. The man grabs the woman breast and sucks it while his hand is playing with the woman clit to swell it up. Thereafter, the woman use her hand to guide the man's penis into her vagina but can first press the cock against her clit to elicit pleasure and really get wet. She then let the penis in. The woman can wrap her legs around the man's back and put her arms around the man's neck for leverage. To add more sensation and intimacy the hands at the back can be used for a massage. The woman can move up and down or grind her hips in tantalizing circles and from there they can both synchronize moving forth and back in a rhythm. They both can steadily increase the sexual tempo thrusting in that position till they both erupt in an uncontrollable ecstasy.

• **The sidewinder sex position**

The sidewinder sex position is one sex position that partners and couples can use to mesmerize one another in the bedroom. It's one sex position that can give couples the orgasmic thrills they really needs as well as helping them last longer in bed. This sex position enable partners to once in a while stop and make out with some kisses and dry humping before slowing thrusting away to make them last longer. If you are thinking of a tantalizing sex position you will relish with your partner while staying with one another a bit longer, then checking out the sidewinder sex position will be your best option. It will surely make both partners go gaga in sexual excitement. Performing the sidewinder sex position needs both partners laying down and facing each other on the sides. The woman will lift her upper leg so that the man would penetrate from that angle. Then the woman wrap her leg tightly around the man's own legs so that the man can use her muscles and friction to thrust strongly, The woman can keep her legs close together to give the man an extra snug fit for more powerful stimulation. a blowjob can be given to the man by the woman, then she can use her hands to massage his inner thighs, lick his balls then she can tease his penis before sliding it into her mouth . To get the enjoyment of rear entry and the naughty thrills of this sex position but without overly intense stimulation that will birth lesser sex position, the man will penetrate the woman from

101

the rear end as described above position and give some slow thrusting though deeply for longer session and also build orgasmic thrills till they explode in ecstasy that is unimaginable and climax afterwards.

• **Waterfall sex position**

Waterfall sex position is an erotic sex position that partners that needs longer sex session should experiment with, because it one sex position that partners will have a jolly ride pleasuring one another. This sex position gives partners a head rush that is memorable, the sensation that erupts from this sex position during the sex session is heavenly, and you can't go wrong using this sex position if you need a sex position that will enable you last longer with your partner while having real hot sex session. This is one sex position that partners can use to mesmerize one another in the bedroom. With this sex position the man lay on his back on the bed with his shoulders and head hanging down on the floor, then the woman goes on top and then start with foreplay, she can start with the sexy mouth moves to give the man an early arousal by kissing his ears, his neck, his thigh, his stomach and using her hands to give him a massage. She can arouse further by giving him oral sex through licking his balls, sucking his nipples and cock. She can then lower herself slowly on his cock and start thrusting subtly in circles to inhibit quick ejaculation intermittently she let the penis press on her clit to send sexual waves to their body. The woman can go further to squeeze the muscles of your vulva a bit to hold the penis tightly and then increase the tempo of the sensation by riding hard a bit. She can let her booty bounce back and forth before him for more visual appeal and to induce the man to unconsciously moan and scream in ecstasy. She can take a break for more caresses and kisses before riding harder this time to climax.

• Sofa surprise position

This is a sex position that one can perform anywhere on the bed, in the bathtub, the kitchen etc so don't be deceived by the name because it isn't only restricted to your sofa. This is almost like the Asian cowgirl sex position where the woman is on top of the man which both partners enjoy a lot. So if partners want a long lasting steaming sex session with earth quaking orgasm then trying out this sex position will be their pleasure. The man sit on a sofa or anything else and the woman squat down on the man from a standing position facing the man so that man would enter her from that angle, the woman will need to be flexible here since she will be squatting far low, then the man can stimulate the woman and get her really wet before penetrating through this angle. The woman can lift her butt a bit so that the man can penetrate the wet pussy conveniently, penetrating deep so that the penis can fill her up, if she is tired of squatting, let her sit on the man's laps and grind on it by pushing her hips forwards and backwards over him. The man can elicit more pleasure by spanking the woman's booty and tingling her nipples. The man can take over with the shallow thrusting which will help keep the session for a long time before orgasm.

• Eyes to the sky sex position

An eye to the sky sex position is one position that gets partners screaming and moaning to the clouds. You can't get it wrong with this naughty sex position if you are really trying to pleasure yourself and also last longer in bed. This sex position will always get couples horny any time they remembers how hot and sizzling it will be when they both get down. So if you are looking for subtle but hot sex position that will give you and your partner intense pleasure and enable you both to last longer too then try out this very juicy sex position. You can start off this tantalizing sex position having the man lie on his back while the woman assume the position on top of the man. The woman can give the man a hand job to get his erection strong enough and the woman should be well lubricated too or the man can use foreplay to get the woman dripping with juice, the woman can use her hand to steady herself on the bed while using the other hand to keep the base of your penis steady as she lower herself on the cock, she then places her back on his chest and they both face the ceiling. Then she start grinding or rocking the man, with this position since it's harder for the man to go deep, he'll last way longer and the drilling will last long so that they get all the sexual pleasure as expected before climaxing.

CONCLUSION

Sex with a partner should be all fun whether as a male or a female, it always good to give your partner hot sizzling sex and drive them crazy with sultry sex positions that will help spice up things in and out of the bedroom. It always good to let your partner have a good G-spot stimulation and generally have a kinky sex while in a relationship with you. It will help to keep the fire of the relationship burning. Funny but true sex matters a lot in a relationship because to some people it the life wire of the relationship without good sex the relationship is good as dead and your partner will think sex with you is boring,

It is always good to still maintain the passion, excitement, fire and orgasm in a relationship; it is not always about having sex but having a sex session that it steamy, adventurous and orgasmic thrilling. So a sex session should have some spanking, naughty and very acrobatic sex styles accompanying it. You want to see your partner screaming, moaning, and being erupt in toe-curling, backing arching and orgasmic thrills then it good to learn new adventurous, crazy and deeper connection sex positions just like the ones we have in this book, there are new and thrilling sex positions that you must try out to get your partner mesmerize in the bedroom.

As earlier stated at the beginning of this book, to get you some very hot and adventurous sex positions that will aid you in your relationship I'm sure by now you would have learned a lot from all the sex positions that have been outlined for each sexual areas of your relationship. The fact is that different sex positions works for different purposes, so you should be trying the different sex position for any sexual needs you really want to achieve in your relationship. With this book we started with chapter 1 on why you need to have sex regularly, of course sex is one of human outstanding needs that needs to be fulfilled and satisfied because it brings about emotional, mental, physical, social, intellectual and health benefits so to have your partner have memorable time with you and become obsess with your body then you should have sex with them regularly.

Chapter 2 will help beginners to satisfy their partners with some easy but sizzling sex positions. It will teach you how not to be a bore in the bedroom and help you dump all the boring antics you have been used to, to make the bedroom a lively place for both of you. It might not be a walk in the park but you can gradually help restore back the flames in and outside your bedroom by using the infallible sex positions I have provided for you in this chapter. There are all tested and trusted sex positions so be rest assured that using them will give you the expected result.

Chapter 3 will definitely help partners with some raunchy positions that can actually stimulate and hit the G-spot. The sex positions provided here will leave partners with huge memorable sensual experience. So to hit that G-spot as expected partners will need to start exploring and experimenting with almost all the sex positions in this chapter. Let the sex session with your partner be steamy hot, put the body on fire and give your partner multiple orgasms at a go

positions like lotus blossom sex position, girl on top sex position, octopus sex position etc. These sex positions will get the woman dripping wet and the man screaming his lungs out.

Chapter 4 will help you get freaky and kinky kind of sex with your partner. You have to take control of all the adventurous sex positions listed in this chapter to spin your partner head and screw your partner out with them. There are very freaky, daring and crazy sex positions but there are sure of fulfilling your expectations if you need volcanic erupting pleasure then try out sex positions like the grinder sex position, spork sex position, the wheelbarrow or the spider sex position and every other ones in this chapter. All these sex positions will make you get to the seventh heavens when you used them. So what are you waiting for go test them out.

Chapter 5 has helped you answer your question on advanced sex positions for better stimulations and stronger orgasm. Your partner will always thank you if you can deliver on the following. What is sex without good level of stimulation and one exploding in multiple orgasms? If this has been bothering you then you have the solution now, chapter 5 has all the sex positions that will help you put your mind at rest. Try out sex positions like the corkscrew sex position, leapfrog sex position, cowgirl's helper position, the trendy cowboy sex position and others on this chapter. Gets your partner asking for more with the sex positions as outlined in this chapter.

Chapter 6 is here for if you really need sex positions that will give you deep connection with your partner and intimacy. You can quench all your lusty desires with all the sultry sex positions that have been listed in this chapter if you need that gluing body contact and sense of belongings then don't forget to go for the spooning, side by side position or the legendary missionary sex positions and with other positions as outlined in this chapter.

Chapter 7 will help you knock partner off with sexual excitement and also have a long lasting sex session. Partners can help themselves quench all the sexual fantasies that they do have in his mind eyes. Through experimenting and exploring the sex positions that are outlined in this chapter. So you need to be up to the task and show your partner that you are more than capable. You should freak him out with the sultry sex positions as highlighted in this chapter.. The sex positions in this chapter will sure help you know how to give your partner spine tingling pleasure, how to tickle his erogenous zones while staying for a good amount of time before driving each other to multiple orgasm . Go try these positions with your partner and see you both last longer as you both moan to highest heavens.

Sex positions for couples is an indispensable companion because you need to armed yourself with it, if you really want to pep up your sexual life, it's a book that is written to be very valuable for you and you are sure of getting your money worth. One thing you should get from this is that you are sure going to get your revving sex life back because this book is going to help you step it up. This book has been written in a way that will not only stimulate your genitals but your minds too, so that you would be motivated to try all the sex positions in each chapter. Use the words of Michelle Obama "just try new things, don't be afraid. Step out of your comfort zones and soar, all right" to motivate yourself. You can't determine your strength if you don't try a thing. So you can start with the simplest of position before going for the crazy and risky ones. Let it be a gradual process for you and your partner.

Finally, I'm convinced that this book have met all your lusty desires of quenching your huge sexual appetite and you will go all out to make your partner happy and get the same doze of happiness too. After reading this book you will have deep connection with your partner, you and your partner will be passionate about sex and the sex positions listed will help you get on the freakier side with your sex life. If you haven't gotten your copy maybe you got this copy from a friend to read then you need to get your own copy and even for your loved ones because this book is a good companion and a friend to everyone. I bet you will be glad you did,

KAMA SUTRA

The Orgasm Bible

Step by step guided potions to connect deeply

with your lover

JESSICA ANDERSON

INTRODUCTION

Romance! Making love!! Sex!!! Call it what you want, but if you're no longer feeling that urge or satisfaction as much as you'd like, then there's going to be a problem. Believe it or not, most marriages that crashed, crashed because they are no longer getting the right satisfaction they want from the relationship. Men cheat on their wives because she doesn't please him anymore. Even women go out of their way to have a sexual partner that will make her feel that spark of romance.

Whatever the case may be, it wouldn't be fair to blame anybody. After all the people that cheat in their marriages or relationships do it with someone else. So, the big question is, what do they have that you don't?

Money? Beauty?

Yes, that counts at times. But the hidden truth is that the surest deal you can seal to keep your man or woman is in the bedroom. I'm not talking about just having a conversation. I'm talking about real hot, hardcore sex that would pop their brains out during orgasm. I bet you'd like to know-how. Well, keep reading!

Have you heard about Kama Sutra? If you have, then things just got a lot easier. If you haven't don't worry, you will get to catch the whole idea as we proceed. You see, a lot of people often don't get the entire concept of Kama Sutra. People think Kama Sutra is all about different sex position and that's all. You wouldn't be entirely wrong if you believe Kama Sutra is about sex positions. However, there's more to it than different sex positions.

Understanding the full benefits of Kama Sutra is one of the major things we'd be looking at in this book. Kama Sutra can help you in your relationship in ways you never thought possible. At times all that your partner needs is someone a little bit more emotional. You shouldn't have sex, like robots!

There was this scenario about a woman who no longer feels like having sex with her husband anymore. She claimed she no longer feels turned on by her husband. She further said all her husband does is to do a little talking, a little kissing and then he's in her, and under 5 minutes he's done and out leaving her completely unfulfilled. To the man, he believes they are having sex, but would you blame her if she cheats.

What about a scenario where a man finds it so difficult to make his woman have an orgasm. Smiles! Don't feel battered if you fall under this category it's one of those midlife crises common among men. Commonly, women don't have an orgasm as fast as men do. Is this true? Well, allow me to let you in on a little secret. Did you know that with the right foreplay and sex position you can make you woman have an orgasm in around 5-10 minutes?

It would interest you to know that Kama Sutra embraces a man approaching and enticing a woman. So, when you want to create that spark of emotion in your woman, there are specific steps you are supposed to take. I'd show you that as we proceed in the book. There are ways a man is supposed to touch a woman to express his desire to have sex with her. There are also ways a woman would react to the approach that would lead the man on further.

Kama Sutra talks about the different types of embrace which we'd be looking at in the book. Then there's also the vital kissing part, which you should do correctly. And of course the sexual-arts, which is an essential part. In all, Kama Sutra talks about sexuality at large.

Did you know that Kama Sutra values women with knowledge? I bet you didn't know that. Our society often ignores the fact that a woman needs to learn how to please her man before getting married. If a woman can learn the different forms of arts, including learning an instrument, solving a puzzle, laying a bed or even playing a word game, it would help her manage her husband and home properly. So, Kama Sutra encourages a woman to be knowledgeable.

Under no circumstance should you have a boring sexual life? Enhance your pleasure nerve and get that ultimate climax you've been craving with Kama Sutra. Find out how in this book. I know everybody has his or her way of having sex. However, if you stick to only one sexual move, how would you know what pleases you more. In this book, I'd also give you a detailed description of how to have nothing less than 10 different sexual positions.

Kama Sutra is one of the most fantastic books written about sexuality. When you have learned ultimately all you need to know about it, you will notice a turn around in your sexual like. I guarantee you! Remember when I told you it is possible to make your woman have an orgasm faster than she used to; with the right gameplay and technique, she'd have multiple orgasms. You also would have the best orgasm you've never had in your life.

Kama Sutra is very beneficial in all aspects. And this book would enlighten you on all you need to know about Kama Sutra. When you're done reading this book, you can be sure that your partner would love you more. You'd notice your partner wants to be around you always and they always feel turned on by you. All these secrets are in this book, so keep reading.

Also, I perceive you are having a weird feeling about the whole idea of Kama Sutra and all. You may probably be thinking right now that you love all that you've been hearing, but you don't seem to know how to bring the whole game changer to your life and the bedroom.

Well, you can talk to your partner about it, they might understand. But if you feel talking to your partner about Kama Sutra is out of the picture, don't worry, there are other ways you can maneuver it into your relationships. So, don't worry, in this book, I'd also teach you how to bring Kama Sutra into your life.

When you start applying Kama Sutra in your relationship, the result is fantastic. So, don't think about it too much. Our past is past, and there's nothing you can do about our past. So, don't live in the past. The future isn't here yet, but we dream of how we want it, despite that don't live in them. Instead of living in the past or present, live in the present and what you do currently. So, take a bold step today and learn more about the Kama Sutra.

CHAPTER 1:
WHAT IS KAMA SUTRA?

When you hear the word Kama Sutra, what comes to your mind? Now, if sex comes to your mind, then you're on track. Kama Sutra is an ancient Sanskrit Indian text written on emotional fulfillment, eroticism, and sexuality in life. You shouldn't think of Kama Sutra as a manual on sexual positions, because it is not. Although Kama Sutra talks about sex position, but it isn't a manual, like the manual you get for your TV. You know your TV manual tells you to press the on button to switch the TV on, the Kama Sutra doesn't work that way. Instead see the Kama Sutra as a guide. Kama Sutra as a whole was written as a guide to the nature of love, maintaining one's love life, finding a life partner, and the art of living. Kama Sutra also talks about other aspects as it relates to pleasure- oriented faculties in our lives.

So, it would be wrong of you to expect to read the Kama Sutra and expect it to work like 1 + 1 = 2. It doesn't work that way. Kama Sutra is an art, and to fully enjoy the pleasures thereof; you need to understand the art as a whole. And when you know the technique, you'd know how to apply it as it affects you in your life. What works for me in my bedroom might be different from what works for John Doe. What makes girls attracted to me might be different from what makes girls attracted to you. So, the Kama Sutra is a guide that shows you how to use what you have to your advantage.

Kama Sutra is one of the oldest Hindu text about erotic love that has survived till date. It is a literary text with concise aphoristic verses that have survived even into the modern era with different commentaries and expositions. The Kama Sutra is a mix or Anustubh-meter and prose verses. One thing about the text I love so much is that it acknowledges the Hindu concept of Purusharthas (righteousness, prosperity, love, and spiritual values). It also lists desire, emotional, and sexual fulfillment as one the proper goal in life.

Basically speaking, Kama Sutra talks about a whole lot of things that can benefit our lives. But before we dive deeper into the benefits of Kama sutra, let us do a little background check on Kama sutra.

Background of Kama Sutra

The Hindu tradition holds the concept of Purusharthas as vitality for human sustenance. Now, the Purusharthas is divided into four main goals as already stated above. Dharma signifies righteousness, Artha signifies prosperity, Kama signifies love with or without sexual connotations, and Moksha signifies spiritual values. These four outlines are necessary for any human being to live a fulfilling and happy life.

Other lingual like Dharmasastra, Kamasastras, Arthasastras, and Mokshasastras genre have all done the same study on sexuality. As at the time they were making their studies, they saved their texts in palm leaves. Funny enough, most of these palm leaves has survived many years.

Kama sutra itself belongs to the Kamasastra genre of texts. Another example of Sanskrit text on emotions and sexuality is the Anangaranga, Ratirahasya, Panchasayaka, Nagarasarvasva, and Kandarpachudamani.

Professor Laura Desmond, is an anthropologist, and professor of Religious Studies. He claims that one of the defining objects of Indian Kamasastra literature is the harmonious sensory experience from a good relationship between yourself and the world. When you can understand this fully, you would be able to enhance your sensory capabilities in a way that it affects and can be affected by the world. Kama sutra has profited many such that it has been able to survive so many years.

Basically speaking on the Kama Sutra, it has survived via many versions throughout the Indian subcontinent. In an attempt to get the right translation of the Sanskrit Kama text in Anangaranga (a lingual widely translated by the Hindus in regional languages like Marathi), the associates of the British Orientalist Richard Burton came in contact with a part of the Kama sutra. In no time, the Brits had an intense love for the little portion of the sutra they had. They even commissioned the Sanskrit scholar Bhagvanlal Indraji to locate the complete Kama sutra, and translate the manuscript.

Indrajit did as commissioned, locating different variants of the manuscripts from libraries and temples of Varanasi, Jaipur, and Kolkata. Richard Burton then published a translated English edition of the manuscript, although it was not a critical edition of the Kama Sutra Sanskrit. According to S.C. Upadhyaya, there were issues with Richard Burton published manuscripts that has survived. The text likely went through a lot of revisions over time. This was, however, confirmed by other 1st millennium CE Hindu texts on the Kama. There was mention and cite in the Kama Sutra and some quotations that credited the Kama Sutra by some historical authors, and were not found in his text of Kama Sutra that survived.

However, Vatsyayana, an ancient Indian philosopher is the first author to translate the Sanskrit text into English originally. He mainly discusses the Kama text based on its relationship with Artha and Dharma. However, he made some mentions of the fourth aim of life in some of the verses.

All being said, enough of the names and languages, let's proceed forward a little bit. At least by now, you already know the basics of the Sanskrit Kama, as well as the major for aims in life the Kama Sutra is all about.

What does Kama Sutra talk about?

Having said all that about the history and built a solid foundation of where Kama Sutra came from, let's go deeper. Now, let me enlighten you a bit on what the book talks about. In Vatsyayana's Kama Sutra, there were 1250 verses and 36 chapters in 64 sections, and it was infused in 7 books.

Kama Sutra makes use of a combination of prose and poetry to narrate the dramatic fiction of two characters, Nayika (Woman) and Nayaka (Man). These characters were aided by other characters like Vita (Pander), Pitamarda (Libertine), and Vidushaka (Jester). What is doing by these characters can be subdivided into five main acts. Allow me to break down the happenings below.

Flirting and Courtship

A couple of acts in the text includes several events and happenings where the subjects were flirting, which resonates in the modern era today. For instance, there was a place that suggests that if a man, not just any man, a young man, to be precise, seeks to attract a woman, he should hold a party. And at the party, he should invite guests to recite poetry. In the modern-day, we can replace poetry with something else. Perhaps a Dj, or a rapper, or a singer would suffice for a perfect replacement of the poet. Another example is a text from Kama Sutra that suggests a boy and a girl should play together, probably go swimming in the river. Then the boy should dive into the water away from the girl he likes. The boy should then swim under the water to her, then surprise her by touching her gently from her legs upwards, then dive in again and swim away from her. In the modern era, you can still try this, and it works perfectly every single time. Even if you are at the beach, river, swimming pool, it all works perfectly well with this tip.

Book 3 of Kama Sutra talks mainly in the art of courtship with the aims of marriage. At the opening verse of book 3, there is a declaration that marriage should be a conducive means of purely natural love between partners. The first three chapters of the book talks about how a man needs to find the right bride. And the fourth chapter is about how a woman can get the man she desires.

Intimacy and Foreplay

Vatsyayana's Kama Sutra also describes foreplay and intimacy in many forms before and during sex. In this part, that is where we'd talk about foreplay like the embrace. In Kama Sutra, embrace (Alingana) is discussed in eight forms. These eight forms of Alingana includes Sphrishtaka, Viddhaka, Udghrishtaka, Piditaka, Lataveshtitaka, Vrikshadhirudha, Tilatandula, and Kshiranira. In embrace text from Kama Sutra, the first four are grouped into what is called expressive mutual love, which is rather non-sexual. The other four are grouped into increased pleasure during foreplay and during sexual intimacy.

And for the intimacy part of the Kama text involves kissing (Chumabanas). The text suggests that there are twenty-six different types of kisses. The types of kisses range from those kiss that shows affection to those that shows respect, and then during foreplay and sex. Vatsyayana also made mention of the different kissing practices in different parts of ancient India. Other forms of intimacy and foreplay include, holding, and embraces, rubbing, and mutual massage. Intimacy and foreplay also include biting and pinching, hands to stimulate, and using fingers, three styles of French kissing, and different styles of cunnilingus and fellatio.

Adultery

You'd probably wondering what the Kama Sutra says about adultery, right? Well, there are about 16 verses in the Sutra that talks about the reasons why a man is free to seduce a married woman. Vatsyayana also mentions several types of urban girls who are unmarried virgins, some were married but abandoned by husbands, and others were windows looking to remarry and courtesans.

Vatsyayana also encouraged young ones to learn how to earn a living. He further continued that because their young age is for pleasure, and as the years pass, they should concentrate on living virtuously and hope to escape the circle of rebirth. Kama Sutra teaches a man adulterous sexual affairs in a way that it allows a woman to assist him such that it works against his enemies and also facilitates his successes.

In the Sutra, there are citations which explain the signs and reasons why a woman wants to go into an adulterous relationship. It also explains the reasons why she does not want to commit adultery. The Kama Sutra teaches the strategies on how to engage in an adulterous relationship. However, it concluded the chapter on sexual affairs, stating that it is not advisable for anyone to go into an adulterous relationship. The Sutra claims that adultery benefits only one side of the marriage and not the two sides, thereby leaving the other hurting. Moreover, adultery goes against Artha and Dharma.

Caste, Class

When talking about uniqueness, Kama Sutra is a unique sociological and cultural milieu of ancient India. There is a near-total disregard for caste (jati) and class (varna) in Kama Sutra. The human relationship as it pertains to different sexual type are not segregated either was it repressed by caste or gender. In the pages of Kama Sutra, the lovers are not high class, neither were they, low class, either, they were at least rather rich enough to dress and wear proper clothing. The characters also pursuit after social leisure activities, and buy surprise gifts for their lovers.

The only rare mention of caste (i.e., High class) was in a text when a man was finding his legal wife and also advice about stories on how to seduce a woman especially other virgins of the same jati (castes). Generally, the text talks about sexuality between a man and woman across different caste and class both in rural and urban settings.

Same-sex, Group-sex Relationships

Lastly, Kama text also talks about homosexual relationships, such as oral sex between two women, as well as between two men. Lesbian relationships are covered mainly in chapter 5 and 8 of Vastyaayana's Kama Sutra. Same-sex relationships were explained in Kama Sutra through the notion of the third sexuality (Tritiya Prakriti).

The text discusses that there are two sorts of third nature. The first third nature is when a man behaves or thinks he's a woman. The second notion is when a woman behaves of think she's a man. There is a long conservative text in the Sutra that talks about a man dressed in a woman's apparel having fellatio with another man. There are also places where a two-woman losing their virginity with each other using their fingers, as well as sex toys and oral sex.

In this book, we'd be talking about everything Kama Sutra. We'd be featuring how to kiss and caress your partner, massage, foreplay, as well as different ways of making love. So, sit back and relax as we take you on an adventure.

CHAPTER 2:
HOW CAN I APPLY THIS TO MY LIFE IN THE MODERN DAY

It is no surprise if you have this question in your mind. The Kama Sutra is an ancient book. And as we'd have it, times have changed. But has our sexual desires as humans evolved? Well, the short, simple answer to that is no. It's pretty much the same. And if you'd ask me what I feel, well, I think the ancient guys had their sexual life figured out than we do. So, if you want to know how to apply Kama Sutra to your life in the modern world, stick around.

No matter how time changes, our want for a loving, and desirable and compassionate partner that we can connect with would never change. In the Hindu tradition where Kama Sutra sprang out from, saw the human body as a vehicle that is used to express spirituality and not as the West see it for many centuries as a sinful thing. Sex is famed as a sacrament and the joy of having sex. The wall carving and erotic status in many Hindu temples is an indication of the celebration of sex.

The bottom line is that sex should not be worshipped, as many people do in the modern world. To truly enjoy sex to the fullest, you need to take it from the grass root, and then build it up to something great. Seeing a lady in a bar, and you walk up to her to buy her a drink, and after 5 minutes of conversation, you guys are already in a room having sex. And in 10 minutes you are done – that isn't sex. What you guys are indulging in, is called FUCKING! Fucking is different from having sex or making love.

Fucking is when all you guys care about is the penis and the vagina. When all other factors is equal to zero, when you care more about you having an orgasm, then that is fucking. Fucking can be somewhat greedy, because all you care about is yourself, and your pleasure. But on the other hand, real sex takes more than just the penis and vagina to have. To have real sex, it doesn't start with clothes going off.

Real sex takes time; it builds up; it grows, and all the little things you do before and during sex, is what makes it real sex. There are also lots of emotions flying everywhere when having real sex; it's more like your partner is in your head, stimulating all the right places. It's more like when you're being touched right at that spot you want every single time.

Many people have fucked, but very few have had real sex. But don't worry, because today, we're going to be talking about everything you need to know about having that deep connection. Now to introduce Kama Sutra and start having real sex in this modern world, there are some few steps you need to take. So, without any further ado, let's get right into the details.

Preparing the Body

The first and most crucial part about introducing the Kama to the bedroom is by first preparing the body. Preparing the body can be equated with cleanliness. It starts with you as an individual. If you want to bring this whole Kama story into reality in your life in a modern-day, then you need to take your cleanliness seriously.

As a man or as a woman, when you wake up in the morning, brush your teeth, use the toilet, take your bath. It doesn't matter if you're married or single; it applies to everyone. Preparing the body should be done individually. But if you feel you have a deeper connection with your partner and you don't mind doing it together, kudos to that.

As a man always try to do a little work out in the morning so that your body would feel fit. If possible, a walk or jog around the block would suffice. And if you can do more exercise to have a somewhat fit or athletic physique that would equally work. Before you go out for the workout, (if you're jogging) make sure you brush your teeth. Also, make sure you don't wear a sweaty clothes (meaning make sure you don't have a bad body odor). The reason why you should care is that you never know who you might run into, so it's better if you're always prepared.

As a woman, you should also do the same. You should also do a little workout, so you don't lose your body shape. Brush your teeth regularly and take your bath regularly. Don't always wait till you have a smelling body odor oozing out before your shower. As a man or a woman, when preparing your body, there are two essential things you need always to do either together or alone.

Perfuming the Breath

An odor from any part of the body dampens sexual passion. No matter how high in the sexual spirit, you think you may feel, a big mood-killer is an odor. And what is even worse is when you combine body odor with bad breath that alone would kill the mood stone dead. The Kama text highly recommends that as a person, you should improve on your breath for better sexual experience. Luckily for you, there are a couple of breath freshener in the market you can get. In Vatsyayana's Kama Sutra, he suggested betel leaves, and you'd agree with me that most of the breath freshener out there today are better. So, this should be to your advantage in being in the modern-day.

A lot of people who are suffering from bad breath today don't even know they have bad breath. And most times, because their partner does not want to sound offensive or rude, they don't mention it, which usually causes a lot of problems. So, feel free to ask your partner to be honest with you if you have bad breath. At least your partner would feel more comfortable disclosing whether you have bad breath or not if you requested him or her to tell you. However, in a case where the mouth odor is rather intense, you should seek medical advice rather than disguising the problem with mouth freshener.

Bathing Together

Bathing together is another way of preparing the body to bring Kama teachings into the bedroom in a modern world. When you and your partner take a shower together or share a bathtub, it sets the mood right. It takes away the grime of the day, and it also creates an atmosphere for love. The two of you can also add a little foreplay to the picture. For whatever makes you feel comfortable. Don't be too pushy; likewise, don't restrict yourself to just bathing alone.

Always pay attention to your partner's body languages. Know when they want more of you, and when they want their space. If they want their space, it means you haven't quite set the mood right, and you need to try another approach. The takeaway message is that you make sure you do what makes you both comfortable and don't force yourself to enjoy the moment. True lovemaking comes naturally.

The Erogenous Zones

Another approach from the Kama teachings that can be brought to the bedroom in a modern-day is the erogenous zones. The erogenous zones or better still the pleasure zones are those parts of the body that turns your partner on, sets them in the mood. It is said that the brain is the most potent sexual organ, which is very accurate. The brain is one of the most important parts of sex, and engaging it while making love is very vital as well. Lovemaking without the imagination free play is more like a soulless mechanical activity; better still we call it fucking.

As good lovers, it's essential to have an imaginative and sensitive appreciation of those parts of each other's body that are referred to as erogenous zones. No sexually active person would deny the fact that the genitals are the primary erogenous zones. However, other erogenous zones needs to be tapped in other to have the potential erotic and extreme joy of making love. For example, the brain, and the skin are two more primary erogenous zones that shouldn't be left out of the picture.

Concentrating on just the primary erogenous zones of the body and leaving out the myriads of other erogenous zones is like eating part of a well-balanced diet and then leaving the remaining part out. Kama Sutra speaks widely on the topic of pleasure zones and that they should be exploited. Of kissing, for instance, Kama text suggested some places that should be kissed, like the lips, in the mouth, the cheeks, throats, forehead, and so on.

There are also other pleasure zones like the breasts, the nipples, buttocks, earlobes, feet, and the list goes on and on. Some people are turned on by having their calves touched and inside their arm. And for others, it could be anywhere on their skin. Let me enlighten you on these pleasure zones.

Lips and Throats

To some people, a kiss on the lips or at the throat is what sets them in the mood. So a spine-tingling aroused, a light kiss or lick around the throat would suffice. You could also lightly touch the throat as well. Many people have successfully used these erogenous zones to seduce a lot of women. Now you know the drill, feel free to try it out as it works perfectly fine in a modern world.

Best Foot Forward

The best foot forward talks about everything you need to know about the foot, and it's erogenous zones. There are reflex connections in the feet as well as the rest of the body. When these reflex connections are stimulated, we feel goose pimples all over our body (you should be able to relate with this). The sensation flows from the limbs to the rest of the body, especially the head. Some people only relate to feet and sex to foot fetishism. However, the pleasures of the feet go way deeper. Here are some erogenous zones on the feet that sets the right mood.

Ankles and calves: You can have some surprising sensual feelings by simple stimulating some parts of the ankles, toes, and calves. While grooming the body for sex, you can occasionally slide your hands around your partner's body and locate these points. You can also combine it with a soft, gentle kiss on their lips to even set the mood higher up.

Thighs: The tights are also very sensitive parts for both male and female. It's muscular and soft. So, a lot of feelings goes on around there. You can also slide your hand in the sensitive inner thigh of your partner. You could even slide it further down, and go closer to the genitals, and play around it. You could also place a kiss on the thigh or lick around it with your tongue for real erotic pleasure.

Buttocks: buttocks is one of the most popular erogenous zones. The buttocks are richly enriched with nerve cell, so every squeeze and spanking goes a long way. It all depends on what you're partner prefers. Use the body language of your partner to decide.

Sensual Skin

The skin is the largest organ we have, as it is one of the erogenous zones; it should be one of the most exploited. The skin is sensitive to the lightest touch and the smallest change to temperature and pressure. There are also over 1500 sensory receptors in the skin, so yes it very touch sensitive. Although the sensual feeling from the skin depends on the part or erogenous zone touched.

The Breasts: The woman's breast has a significant role it plays in sexual attraction. It doesn't only attracts the man but it also an undeniable pleasure zone for the woman, and the man. The nipple areas are surrounded by areolae, which are highly sensitive to touch. So, when you rub her nipples softly, it gets to her head. At times when you combine it with a little sucking, it gets deep into her head, which is characterized by her closing her eyes to enjoy the full pleasure thereof. At times while squeezing her nipples and breasts, she could bite her lips and stare intensely at the man to give him a devout, please.

The Buttocks: a lot of men find a woman's buttock very attractive. It doesn't end there because the buttock is also a sensitive, sensual part of the skin. The buttocks can be a pleasure house and an attractor. It can be mutually stimulating when a man squeezes, and lightly slaps the buttocks. He could also kiss and bite the buttocks gently. The woman, on the other hand, can also indulge in the act and find it as enjoyable too. For a slight variation in the ways you want to stimulate the buttocks, you can try using light strokes combined with loses and gentle but firm squeezes and kneading.

Anal sensitivity: lastly, there is anal sensitivity. For many who haven't tried anal sex before, you might want to consider trying it. Anal sex might be somewhat painful at first, but it's very pleasurable. For stimulating the anal, you could start with your fingers. Imagine a clock face on your partner's anus, and 12 o'clock hand being the part that points to the tentacles or the vagina. Using that clockface imagination of your partner's anus, locate 2 o' clock, and 10 o' clock as they are the most sensitive points.

Creating the Mood

The same way it is important to prepare the body, as well as it is to locate the erogenous zones, it is equally important to create the right mood. In creating the right mood, there are a couple of things you can use to create the right atmosphere which would give room for the right mood to set in. One of the first suggestion is to make sure that if the weather is hot, make the room refreshingly cool. Also in cold weather, make the room warm enough, but don't make it stuffy. Having background music also helps to create the right mood. However, the music shouldn't be too raucous or agitated, but something conducive and tender, but not too soporific so you don't feel sleepy. Despite the way loving making is done in the modern world in the Kama text things are a bit different, you'd agree with me that by following the Kama text, you'd do better. Here are some quick tips on what you can use to create the right mood.

Flowers

Flowers has been one of everyone's favorite things when making love. Flower is a perfect way of connecting us to that inner feeling we have inside. When you want to create the perfect environment in your room for lovemaking, sprinkles fresh fragrant flowers like roses in the room.

You can use the roses to decorate and perfume your room so that when you both step into the room, the whole atmosphere just seems perfect and out of this world. Everything quickly falls into place when the flowers are red.

Soft Light

Another idea you should engage in is making use of soft light. The light shouldn't be too dull so that you can still see each other. Likewise, the light shouldn't be too bright, so the atmosphere doesn't seem too busy. You could set gently flickering glow of candlelight in your room as they are more romantic than electric light. For safety reasons, keep candles away from curtains bedding or any flammable materials in the room. You can swap make use of scented candles as they lit the room and equally perfume it as well. Candles are generally preferred because they create a kind of soft and seductive light.

Scenting the Room

Scenting the room is equally important when trying to create the right mood. Anything that makes the nose work has an indirect connection with the brain. Having a nice scenting room is a perfect way to seduce any woman. You can also make use of seductive scented like invents scented crystals, or heated essential oil. Whichever type of scent you decide to use, all works perfectly.

Champagne and Silk

Having a bottle of well-chilled vintage champagne with seductive silk lingerie or nightmare goes a long way in making the environment even more perfect. For a romantic evening, whether at a hotel or home, be sure to indulge in using silk and champagne.

Perfuming the Skin

I have spoken about this point before, and I don't want to overemphasize on it, as you also ready know what you need to do. Have a nice body fragrance. When you have your bath, use a delicately scented bathing oil to perfume your skin. And if you're more of a shower kind of person, use a scented shower gel. Always make sure you gave a fresh body fragrance.

Oil and Lotions

To make your foreplay even more seductive, engage in using oils and lotions. Using scented massage oil and lotion on each other's skin is even more pleasurable. There are different ways in which you can give each other a sensual massage; we would talk more about it later in this book.

CHAPTER 3:
HOW TO INTRODUCE KAMA SUTRA TO THE BEDROOM IN TODAYS WORLD

In this chapter of the book, we'd be talking about how to introduce Kama sutra to the bedroom in today's world. I would be using teachings from the Kama sutra to explain how it still applies to our sexual lives even in the modern world.

There is this particular teaching from the Kama text that particularly caught my attention, and I would be sharing it with you. It talks about touching and caressing. When you look deep into touching and caressing, although it's still a part of foreplay, there is more to it than meets the eye. What interested me the most is that the best strategy to use to introduce Kama teachings to the bedroom in a modern world is by using the lessons of touching and caressing from Kama Sutra.

Touching and caressing is a vast topic to cover. You can even use a part of touching and caressing to connect with your partner deeply. We'd cover this part of touching and caressing in the next chapter. But in this chapter, we'd focus on the part of touching and caressing you can use to introduce Kama teachings to the bedroom in a modern world.

There are a couple of things for you to learn from this text. So, I suggest you get your learning mind up and ready to receive a newly added knowledge to get you on track. So, let's get right into it.

What is touching and caressing?

Touching and caressing is an act of physically stimulating your partner's erogenous zones for pleasurable sensual moments. Touching and caressing is a form of foreplay generally encouraged to be done before sex and during sex. There are different types of touching and caressing, and each comes with its advantages over the other.

When you touch a particular part of your partner's body, and it feels very sensual, it doesn't mean you're to only concentrate on only that part. A combination of different stimulation of the various erogenous zones is what leads to great lovemaking.

Under touching and caressing from the Kama teachings, there are five major lessons I will be covering in this book. These lessons include embracing, mutual grooming, sensual massage, scratching, and hair play. These different lessons are what we are going to use to explain this chapter and the next. In other words, you can use the teaching from touching and caressing to introduce the Kama into the bedroom and also profoundly connect with your partner. In this chapter, we would be talking mainly on embracing and mutual grooming.

Embracing

Embracing from the Kama Sutra is divided into up to eight different kinds. Of the eight types of embracing, they are divided into two groups. The first group includes four kinds of embrace which talk about different embracing that indicates the mutual love between a man and a woman coming together. The first group comprises embracing such as the touching embrace, the rubbing embrace, the piercing embrace, as well as the pressing embrace.

This second group of embrace also includes four types of embrace that involves a somewhat more intimate kind of embrace. This group of embrace consists of the mixture of sesame seed with rice embrace (Tila Tandulaka), climbing a tree embrace (Vrikshadhirudhaka), the twinning of a creeper (Jataveshtitaka), and the milk and water embrace (Kshaniraka).

Apart from these significant types of embrace, you can quickly learn and use in the bedroom; the Vatsyayana Kama also talks about four different ways you can embrace simple members of the body. These include simple members of the body like the breasts, thighs, the forehead, and the middle part of the body (Jaghana). Having a full understanding of how the embrace works would give you a complete insight into how to introduce the Kama into the bedroom in a modern-day. So, without further ado, let's dive into the details of how this embrace works.

1. The First Group of Embrace

In this group of embrace, we would be talking about a little bit, not too intense way to embrace your partner. This types of embrace do not have too much sensual feeling in it, and you can easily practice it even when you do not want to have sex. And on the topic of embrace, here is takeaway advice, using a couple of embraces mixed with other foreplay is a perfect way to start lovemaking. All you need to take note of are your partner's soft spots. Triggers those sweet spots and combine it with the right embrace and you'd find everything falling into place.

This group of embrace is straightforward, and sometimes can even be practiced in public places. There isn't really much to this group of embrace. Also, a lot of people practice most of the embrace in this group without even knowing it belongs to this group. What I am trying to say is that it is the most common type of embrace out there. The benefits of this embrace is that it is straightforward and can be used to lure your partner easily. So, when you really want to introduce the Kama into the bedroom, be sure to start with any one of the embraces in this group.

1) The Touching Embrace

The touching embrace is a type of embrace whereby the man stands in front of the women and their body touches. This embrace is all about making sure your bodies touch; you feel the warmth of your partner's body. Your bodies should also touch in a way that you feel the texture of your partner in a way that you can tell how soft or hard your partner's body is.

This type of embrace can be a playful way of showing erotic affection to your partner. Take, for instance, when you step into the room, and your partner walks up to you with arms wide open. And the man shoves you into his arms. And you as the woman falls into his arms and find that comfort spot, where you can feel his body warmth, and soft but a bit rigid muscles. And then you dim your eyes a bit with a little smile on your face. That scenario is a perfect example of a touching embrace. Note that the key point of this embrace is the bodies coming in contact.

2) The Rubbing Embrace

The rubbing embrace, on the other hand, is a type of embrace where two partners rub their bodies together. For instance, imagine two lovers walking down a dark street, or a public place like a resort, or somewhere a bit lonely. When these two lovers in this scenario rub their bodies against each other as they walk is called the rubbing embrace. This type of embrace is best done when you are in public or walking together. This type of embrace is mainly common among the younger ones when walking together with their arms tightly around their partner's waist.

Nonetheless, you can perfectly practice this embrace even in the house. In the kitchen, for example, when you're both fixing a meal, perhaps you want to go to the other side of the kitchen, you can pass by your partner, and rub your body against theirs with a big smile on your face. There are different ways you can apply the rub embrace; the main point here is to rub your body against each other. I said rub, not hold or press, that the main difference, the rubbing part.

3) The Pressing Embrace

The pressing embrace is one of my favorite types of embrace. This type of embrace is a lot more sensual, with a whole lot of emotions attached to it. This type of embrace is very similar to the touching embrace, but the main difference between the two is that the touch embraces the main objective is to make sure there is contact. But for the pressing embrace, the main objective is to make sure that there isn't just contact, but the contact is deep and forcibly against your partner's body.

In this type of embrace, the woman can even feel the man's heart beating because of how tight the body would be pressed against each other. This embrace is mostly given when a party misses the other, and they want to get all they have missed in a big hug. This type of embrace is very common among young lovers as they get pinned to the wall or pillar by their lover. Being pinned to the wall or pillar by a lover is a type of embrace only a few people would object to.

4) The Piercing Embrace

Lastly, the piercing embrace is a type of embrace that is even more sensual than the pressing embrace. If you try to figure out what this embrace means from the name would clearly misdirect you as the word piercing used is merely a figure of speech and not a literal description. What the piercing embrace is all about is when a woman brushes her breast against her man as she bends.

To perform this embrace, let's do a little bit of imagination. Imagine a man sitting or standing whichever one you prefer, then imagine a woman in front of him and his hands around her waist. Now that you have that picture in your mind, that perfect, now imagine the woman bending backwards as though she wants to pick something from the floor. She doesn't need to bed too backward; the aim is to expose her breast.

Now, as the breasts are exposed, the man grips her even closer to his bosom, and the embrace is complete as he feels the warmth and softness of her breast. This type of embrace is very sensual and has a lot of emotion attached to it.

2. The Second Group of Embrace

This group of embrace is a combination of embracing and lovemaking. This group of embrace is very sensual and very stimulating. This type of embrace can also be adopted during the congress or lovemaking. Don't worry yourself too much about the names of each of the embrace; I know they sound a bit off. But the main thing you should focus your mind on is understanding how the embrace works. Here are the four types of embrace in this group.

1) The Milk and Water Embrace

If you are still new into the whole love game, and you and you're very much into each other, then this type of embrace is perfect for you. Although this type of embrace and lovemaking might be a bit painful, because you and your partner are too much in love with each other, you wouldn't be thinking of any hurt or pain.

To perform this embrace, imagine a man in a seated position on a chair or on the bed and the woman on his lap. As the man sits with a full-blown penis, the woman comes and sits on it as she embraces him with her hands around his back, and the man's hand around her back as well. Lovemaking would be a lot slower, but it would be very passionate. Lovers would try these types of embrace and lovemaking eventually lose themselves to each other in their physical relationship.

2) Climbing a Tree Embrace

Climbing a tree embrace is a pretty simple embrace to perform. In this embrace, the woman places one of her feet on the foot of her lover, and the other foot is placed on one of his thighs. One of her arms also goes round to his back, and the other one stays on his shoulder. She could also talk dirty like how she would want the make to fuck her or so whatever turns the man on. Then she should try as though she is making an attempt to climb his for a kiss.

As her leg is on one of the man's thighs, he should go for the penetrations. Also, note that this type of lovemaking might also be somewhat painful. But with the amount of love as well as other factors between lovers, make them ignores this pain.

3) The Mixture of Sesame Seed with Rice Embrace

The mixture of sesame (Sesamum) seen with rice embrace is a type of embrace lover do while lying down on the bed. In this embrace, the lovers lie on the bed and embrace each other closely, with arms and thighs of one of the lovers encircled by the arms and thighs of the other lover. In that position, they rub their thighs and arms against each other while they make love as it were like the mixture of sesamum seed with rice.

From the name of this embrace, the sesame seed with rice signifies the thighs and the arms of the lovers, and the mixture signifies them rubbing together. The main aim of this embrace is to have maximum skin-to-skin contact.

4) The Twining of a Creeper Embrace

Lastly, we would be looking at this type of embrace in this group. Kama Sutra describes this embrace as when a woman clings to her man as a creeper twines around a tree. The man then bends his head down to as he reaches to kiss her. And then he makes a little sound like shh, as they embrace. And then the woman looks lovingly towards him and have a cute smile on her face.

In this embrace, as the man put your hands around her back as though you supporting her from falling back. And the woman holds the man's neck with one hand and leaned her head towards the man's shoulder. One of the woman's legs also goes to the side of the man's thigh as the man holds it with his second hand. Then the embrace is complete with that passionate look.

3. Embracing Simple Members of the Body

The main aim of embracing the simple members of the body is the arousal of the male desire. It includes embracing simple parts of the woman's body with the intention of causing arousal in the man's desire. There are four types of embracing simple members of the body. Although in the holy book of Kama, there are orders in which embrace should be followed; however, in a case where the wheel of love sets in, there are no motion and no order.

1) Embracing the Thighs

You may be wondering how embracing the thighs can help in introducing the Kama to the bedroom, well it is because it causes arousal. To perform this type of embrace is done when a lover presses forcibly one or both of the thighs against the partners own. In an attempt to bring the thighs together, you would feel your genitals touching each other, which would cause an increase in your desire and arousal. This type of embrace is sensual, and you should try it out. As your lover presses their body against yours, on full arousal, the lover can move naturally on to intercourse.

2) Embracing the Jaghana

Performing the Jaghana or middle part of the woman's body embrace is one type of embrace you should check out. To perform this embrace, the man presses her Jaghana against your own and mount on her to either bite, scratch with the finger or nail, strike softly, kiss, or play with her hair softly. The Jaghana, according to Kama Sutra, is the area between the thighs and the navel. Clearly, with this type of embrace, congress preludes.

During the congress, as you penetrate her vagina and feel that warm, and wet sensation, you can follow it by sliding your pelvis against her combining it with a circular up and down movement for optimal joy. However, in this modern- day, a lot of lovers often give up on the biting, kissing, and scratching part of this ritual. Although it is not bad if you want to take those parts of the ritual off, the main aim of the embrace is to do what makes you feel comfortable the most.

3) Embracing the Forehead

We can also call this embracing affectionate nuzzling. To perform this embrace with your partner, reach out to your lover and touch their

142

mouth, eyes, forehead with your own. This times of embrace can be used to build up intimacy quickly, confidence with your partner, as well as also enhance arousal. Feel free to engage in this embrace and see where it leads you and your lover.

4) Embracing the Breasts

As a lover, you can also practice embracing the breast as a way to introduce the teachings from the Kama to the bedroom. To perform this embrace, as a man, place your chest or breast between the breasts of your lover. Then press your chest against your lover's breasts so that you can feel the warmth and softness of your lover's breast. An upper body contact like this embrace creates a nipple stimulation for you and your lover. In the end, you would have a higher chance of changing from the usual oral caresses.

Mutual Grooming

In many verses in the Kama Sutra, it was mentioned several times that cleanliness should not be omitted by lovers. Mutual grooming is when you and your lover participate in helping each other stay clean. Mutual grooming can also be seen as a way of preparing the body by lovers for lovemaking. This preparation of the body can include, bathing or showering together, shaving the man's face, washing, drying, and then brushing each other's hair and so on. You can do whatever makes you both feel comfortable.

There are different ways lovers can both mutually groom each other, but we would be focusing on two major ways you can groom each other. Mutual grooming is an indispensable ritual and is highly recommended for lovers. When couples focus their attention to each other's attraction, it can help elevate the anticipation of pleasure.

Mutual grooming can help encourage feelings for trust, tenderness, caring, which will cause each partner to feel a kind of security towards the other. Engaging in any one of the following mutual grooming below can help break down inhibition in a new relationship and also help to reinforce the bonds of an established one.

1) Shaving his beard

From Kama teaching, it is recommended that a man should shave more often than every four days. This act can be somewhat challenging to keep up with. Moreover, having grown beard and looking down at your woman to kiss her can be a mood killer. So, rather than you as a woman telling your man to shave, you can easily do the shaving for him. While you shave your man's beards, make sure you apply enough lather, this is to ensure that you end up with a smooth shave with no cuts.

Don't make the mistake of thinking shaving is for men only. Women also shave; they shave their armpits, legs, and some women shave their pubic hair. Some men prefer their woman to have a hairless pudendum as they find it very erotic. If a woman is also to shave her pubic hair, then she would need to shave it regularly. This is because new hair growth would quickly spring out after a shave, and the new growth would even be stronger and a bit sharp and spiky, which could irritate her lover's skin.

2) Shampooing her Hair

Shampooing your lover's hair is another way you can groom her. Some people even see shampooing her hair as a form of embrace. Although this isn't all that correct because shampooing isn't done during lovemaking, neither is it done for the same reasons embrace is being done. Even though shampooing is not an ideal embrace, it is very sensual grooming. Shampooing is a very intimate experience, especially when shared.

You would agree with me that, as lovers, you enjoy having a soapy bath, and drying each other's body before you go to bed. However, shampooing each other's hair can be a very affectionate moment of grooming, it might not lead to sex at the end of the day. However, it is a great way to start when you want to introduce Kama Sutra to the bedroom in a modern world.

CHAPTER 4:
HOW TO USE THIS TO DEEPLY CONNECT WITH MY PARTNER

Now in this chapter, we would be talking about ways in which you can deeply connect with your partner. This chapter is somewhat a continuation of the lessons we were learning from the previous chapter (chapter 3). We were learning from the lessons of touching and caressing from Kama Sutra and how we can use it to bring Kama Sutra to the bedroom in the modern world. We also learned that under the teachings of touching and caressing, there are five different subdivisions. These subdivisions include embracing, mutual grooming, sensual massage, scratching, and hair play.

From the previous chapter, we also learned that embracing and mutual grooming and two subdivisions of touching and caressing that could be used to introduce Kama Sutra to the bedroom in the modern-day world. However, the remaining three branches of the touching and caressing can be used to connect with your partner deeply. In this chapter, we would be taking a closer look into the remaining subdivisions of touching and caressing and see that we can learn from it.

Sensual Massage

The message is one part of touching and caressing that should not be left out when talking about sex. As humans, we give a lot of references to touch as we tend to link it to sex one way or the other. Sometimes some people fear to touch themselves because of that fear of it being misunderstood. A massage is a form of touch, a very sensual touch that usually preludes congress most times between lovers. One of the most important reasons why people often require massage is to soothe away tension and tiredness.

A lot of lovers often skip or overlook the power of massage, and as such, they miss out on making the body more receptive and relaxed for making love in which they could use to connect with their partners deeply. Whether or not your intention of having a sensual massage session with your partner is to have sex, or not, the main aim of a sensual massage is to create a peaceful and comfortable setting for maximum relaxation. So, whenever you really want to connect with your lover deeply, a sensual massage always has a way of giving it to us.

To have a perfect sensual massage with your lover, a large bed with a firm mattress would do just fine. Or better still, you can place a sheet on the floor, which would be more suitable. Pillows should also be available which would serve as cushions for your lover's neck, back, and ankles. Also make the environment perfect by ensuring it is a bit warm, as well as softly lit. And for the best deepest connection between you and your lover, make sure there wouldn't be any interruption during the massage session. So, if your mobile phone or TV set would be a problem, be sure to do away with it for the time being, or better still switch it off.

There are also different massaging moves that you can use individually or combined with two or more of them. When you start the massage, build them into a full sequence whereby you start from the feet, and you work your way up to the head, and you go back and forth and around. There are different spots in which you are to massage to get the most out of the feeling. But before we look into that, let us first learn the basic massaging strokes. With the right massage stroke at the right spot, you would be a pro masseur or masseuse.

The Basic Massaging Strokes

There are different massage strokes you can use when massaging your lover. However, because of this lesson we are taking, we would be looking at five of the various basic massaging strokes you can use. Take note that whatever massaging stroke you decide to use, you should always try your best to keep your movement symmetrical, even and rhythmic. You should appropriately follow even stroke after the other.

If you want even to make things even more pleasurable, make use of suitable oil. There are different types of massaging oil in which we would also look into that briefly later in this chapter. When you apply the oil, always use the right amount of pressure that agrees with your partner's skin. Since massage is all about pleasure and not pain, be sure to always keep a check on the amount of pressure you are applying. And at times during the massage, you may need to forgo your own pleasure or need and focus on your partner's enjoyment instead. By doing so, you will achieve your goal of being able to give your lover full pleasure. So, without further ado, here are the five different types of basic massaging strokes.

1) Tapotement and cupping

The tapotement and cupping massage stroke is a type of stroke that may involve you making use of both hands. Performing the tapotement massage stroke is more like your lover is lying down on the bed, and you do drumming with a light tapping action on your lover's body. On the other hand, to perform the cupping stroke, imagine your partner still lying down, you would pound his/her body with alternate hands sure that they form a cup with fingers together and your thumbs should be folded in.

2) Hacking

The hacking massage stroke is a type of stroke where you give your loves a series brisk chops with the side of your hand. This stroke is more like using your hand as in karate, but this time a lot gentler. When performing the hacking strokes on your lover's body, make sure you keep your fingers relaxed and not stiff.

3) Petrissage

For this massage stroke, move the balls of your thumb or fingers on your lover's body in a circular kind of motion. This stroke would help your lover soothe away any muscular tension that resides along the spine. Take note not to massage the spine itself as it could be very painful characterized with short sharp pains.

4) Kneading

If you are a fan of baking, if you knead bread dough of whatever type of dough, and you are good at it, then you would be equally as good in this type of massage stroke. To perform this stroke, use your hands to gently knead your lover's flesh in a curved, smooth, and regular movement.

5) Effleurage

The effleurage is a massage stroke that requires you to make use of your palm to glide on your lover's skin. As you glide on your lover's skin be sure to keep your body weight behind the movement, you do not want to put your weight forward, so it doesn't cause you to apply too much pressure. It would help when you make use of this massage stroke first and last on each area of the body your massage.

Using Massaging oil

If you ever decide to make use of messaging oil, be sure to pre-warm it before using it as it works best that way. So, when you pick the pick from its bottle or container, rub them for a few seconds between your hands to pre-warm the oil. When you want to start using the oil, apply it to a small area and attend to it before proceeding to another area rather than applying it to the whole body first before the massage.

After applying the oil to the intended area, follow it up with smooth yet firm strokes. Then when you are through with the massage, leave the oil on the skin to soak. On the other hand, you can wash the oil if you like by rubbing alcohol or gently wiping it off with a towel. However, because this has to be used cold, it might affect the effectiveness of the massage.

If you prefer, you can massage your partner with dry hands. Although massage with dry hands is also great, note that it would be smoother than when you make use of massage oil. There are different types of suitable oil with many gotten from nuts like coconut, and vegetable oils as well. There are also plain oils which are also great for massages such as almond, grapeseed, olive, and sunflower, which can be applied directly to the skin. A lot of people do make use of these plain oil as a base for perfumed essential oil, such as rose, jasmine, ylang-ylang, sandalwood, and patchouli. If you want to make a scented oil for a full massage session, then mix a dozen drop of essential oil with 30ml of base oil.

Different Areas on the Body to Massage

When talking about massage, there are specific areas on the body that should be massaged. On knowing these massaging spots, makes having a sensual massage a lot easier. This is because you would know exactly the right spot to go each time, and that would help you to connect with your partner deeply. There are up to six different areas on the body that should be massaged.

1) Shoulder and Head

A lot of people often when they massage the shoulders and head, they only go for the top of the head, but the action is very similar to that used when washing your partner's hair. However, this is not a grooming move, so it should be more sensual than what you have when grooming each other. The proper way to massage the shoulder and head is to first start by massaging your lover's front shoulder.

Work your way to the sides of your lover's neck as you keep massaging and then cheeks and the jaw. You should not also neglect the temples and forehead. While massaging, you can occasionally run your fingers lightly to the chin and around and over your lover's lips, nose and eyes. As you keep massaging, most of your lover's erogenous zones would be pleasantly sensitized.

2) Back and Spine

When working on massaging the back, make use of gently yet erotic pressure to work your way upward from your lover's buttocks. Try to keep your hands as wildly outspread and level with each other. Also, make your thumbs push inward along you lover's spine as you grind deeper on your partners back.

As you continue the massage in the warm and softly lit room on your lover, work your way up to the base of her/his neck and then out to the shoulders before you then bring your hands down slowly to the sides of her/his buttocks. If your loves being massage in this particular area, feel free to repeat it about ten times or more.

3) Feet and Legs

When you feel like getting the whole massaging spirit to the next level, then you can get to the feet and legs massage. Tell your lover to lie face-down as it would be easier to massage the calves and ankles that way. With your partner at a face- down position, you should sit close so that you avoid straining your back, that way you would not need to stretch forward or bend to reach your partner. Also, hold her leg steadily with one of your hands while you massage it with your other hand.

To start the massage, start by kneading, stretching, and bending each of the feet upward. Then you can proceed by softly rubbing the areas between your lover's feet. Next, run your palm firmly on the soles of the feet and then also rub it along the tops. In turn, raise each of your partner's legs and a few times, rotate each of them until it feels relaxed and loose. Then you can gradually move up the leg and as you do so, pay special attention to the calves, back, and ankles of the thighs and knees. When massaging the feet and legs, there are two types of strokes you can use, the downward leg strokes and the upwards leg strokes.

• *The Downward Leg Stroke*: this is a stroke where you draw you hand smoothly downwards from the ankle to the knee, and then you squeeze the muscle of the calf gently with your fingertips.

• *The Upward Leg Strokes*: this is a stroke where you use the same sorto faction as when you were doing the downward stroke, but this time you are drawing your hand back up from the knee to the ankle.

4) Buttocks

For the buttocks massage, your partner would still need to lie face-down, and you would be sited right beside your partner. Then place your hand on your partner's buttocks to feel the texture of your buttocks as you move your hands in a decisive circular motion. Press the buttock firmly at first for your pleasure and his too. A lot of people enjoy doing a downward buttock stroke; you can try that as well, but, you decide what you and your partner enjoy doing most. After you can then increasingly lightly massage the buttocks until your hands are barely just brushing the skin. You can then continue with squeezing each of the buttocks, in turn, following it with kneading.

5) Arm and Chest

The arm and the chest are other areas of the body perfect for massaging. For optimal pleasure, your partner should lie down facing up for this massage to create a kind of deep connection between the two of you as you can have eye contact. Start this message from the front of the shoulders, and then work your way down to the chest area. You can further proceed to the arms by using a gentle kneading action and again working your way downward.

After that, you can then find your way to the thighs using a kind of circular movement of your hands. To make it easier, rotate your right hand clockwise, and your left hand counterclockwise. Then knead the groin and the thighs and slowly move towards the navel and pubic area. Use gentle pressure when you get to this area because it would be more pleasurable. Then gently pass over the rib too and trace the shape of the pectorals and the breasts with your fingertip as you massage them softly.

6) Upper Back

Lastly, massaging the upper back can help you build a very solid and deep connection with your partner. When you want to massage the upper back, focus more on the muscle between the base of the neck and the shoulder blades. From there, you can bring your hands back down as you follow it with massaging the sides with your fingertips. Reduce the pressure you are using and then knead the back of the neck and shoulders.

Scratching

It is common among lovers to often use their fingernails to scratch their body has an expression of passion. At times scratching could be used to represent reconciliation after you and your lover had a quarrel. During lovemaking, adding a little twist of scratching to the mix can help you create a deep connection with your partner. Although not everyone finds them pleasurable, so always be on the lookout for what pleases your partner.

The Kama Sutra made mention of marks of passion on a young woman's throat or breast as it is a way of telling the world she has a lover. Such marks have always been a thing of admiration right from the times of Vatsyayana and the Kama Sutra. Back in those days, even when a stranger sees a woman with markings of nails on her breast, the stranger would be filled with excitement, love, and respect for her. The same thing applies for men with nail markings on his body.

The Kama Sutra also made mention of scratches as being made by lovers as a reminder of the love they have for each other even when

154

they are apart. So, anytime a lover looks in the mirror and sees the mark, he would be reminded of who puts it there. Or in a scenario where the love keeps feeling slightly uncomfortable itch or a little pain caused by scratch, would also serve as a conviction of the love they have.

Vatsyayana further made mention that wives should not be seen bearing such marks of passion on their body. Although it isn't that it is wrong for her to have one, she is free for her to bear them in private places hidden from everyone else. This is because when a married woman does such, it reduces her respect in public eyes. Vatsyayana further concludes that there is nothing that makes increases love as much as the effects of markings with the nails and biting. So, if leaving passion marks on your livers body is not based on cruelty or anger, then both of you would definitely find it to be fun from time to time.

There are different ways in which harmless passion marks can be used on both partners to express their feelings for each other at the height of excitement during or before intercourse. There are four main types of making this ritualized markings on your lover's body namely, with the back of your hand, with your fingers, with your fist, and with the palm of your hand. Knowing the right ritualized violence for you is dependent on how much violence you enjoy.

Hair Play

The Kama Sutra was very firm when it acknowledges the fascination of the woman's hair is to a man. Kama Sutra further recommends women to learn how to wash, perfume properly, and braid her hair. When a woman knows how to fond and praise her hair, it has the power to arouse feelings of desire in her partner. There are different forms in which lovers can play with hair to deeply connect with each other.

1) The Light Touch

When a woman has a long her, she could make it fall beguilingly over her lover's face and breast, then sensually bushes it against her partner's naked body. And if she is well graced with very long hair, she can enfold her hair on her lover's chest and shoulders. She should be on top in a way that she can sweep it over his entire body teasingly even on his penis so that it heightening his desire for her.

2) Revealing the Neck

A lustrous hair can be a very powerful aphrodisiac and can be inviting lovers to want to play with it and bury his hand in the hair. The texture and sheen of the hair is very attracted to your man. And when she lifts it too reveals a delicate and soft neck, and the joy even gets better.

3) Tactile Pleasure

As a couple, if you want a more intimate relationship that would allow you both to deeply connect with each other as you like, then you need to engage in a loving touch. Running your hand through your lover's hair and plays with the hair would increase the tactile pleasure for both of them.

CHAPTER 5:
KISSING AND MOUTH PLAY IN THE BEDROOM IN TODAYS WORLD

So far, so good, we have learned a lot from the Kama Sutra and how we can apply them to our lives. But now, let's talk about something a little different. Did you know kissing and mouth play, in general, can bring lots of passion to your relationship? A relationship without passion can be a rough one. So I would rather prefer you take advantage of anything that can bring passion to your relationship purely.

Kissing involves the use of your mouth, which is one of the most sensitive parts of the body. You could use your lips or tongue to lick, suck, kiss, and nibble or nozzle areas on your partner's body. Kissing is even art of its own you and your partner can use every day. And Kama Sutra recognizes the benefits of kissing and its different forms. The intensity of the way you kiss your partner has a role it plays on expressing your feelings to your partner. The intensity of a kiss uses a combination of three senses - smell, taste, and touch — each of these parts of the body produces a strong emotional response from your partner. Kissing ranges from fleeting contact to deep penetration with your tongue and so on. Let's dive into it a little bit more.

Types of kissing

There are different types of kissing teachings from the Kama Sutra we would be featuring. You can learn from them and apply then to express a lifting in your relationship. Here are the different types of kissing.

The Bent Kiss

Why not kiss your lover naturally today with this bent kiss. With your head angled slightly on one side which will allow you to get a maximum lip contact. You can even have a deep tongue penetration with this type of kiss, which is very sensual. To perform this type of kiss, gently approach your partner and draw it very slowly as you head tilt to one side. You can pick any side you like - left or right. As you go for the kiss, take it slowly, let the lips touch first then after the full contact you then open your lips and play around with it before going for the deep penetration. You can also place your hand at the back of your partners head as you rub it gently for a more sensual feeling.

The Turned Kiss

If you want to tease your lover and make them feel gentleness and tenderness go for this type of kiss. This type of kiss is also perfect when you want to start foreplay with your partner. Also when you're making love slowly in a face-to- face standing or sitting position.

To perform this type of kiss, one of you, preferable the man turns up the face of his love by holding the chin and head. In that position, he then goes in slowly as your lips touch hers.

The Straight Kiss

When you kiss your love with your heads, you wouldn't be able to have so much of the tongue penetration. This kiss isn't to express an intense passion but a gentle way of showing affection and expression of desire. This type of kiss is recommended for new lovers.

To perform this type of kiss, let your lover sits on your laps and uses your hand to caress, fondle, her body, especially her back while kissing. Then as you go for the kiss, let your heads be angled only slightly, that it would seem almost straight. Then let your lips come in direct contact with each other and enjoy yourself.

Pressed Kiss

This type of kiss is more of an erotic prelude to kissing. It's sensual as you'd feel the contact of your lovers lips. There are two ways you can have this kiss with your lover.

The first method is when you are kissing your lover, and you press your lover's lower lips with force. This kiss expresses the degrees of passion you feel for your lover at that moment. And if you do it right, it can prelude to even more foreplay and clothes go off, and you know the rest.

For the second method, you use your lips to touch your loves lower lips first, then you go for a greatly pressed kiss. This other type of kiss is even more emotional than the first one, so you can choose any one of the two types of pressed kisses to show how much passion is in your heart.

Kissing the Upper Lips

This kissing from the teaching in Kama Sutra, Vatsyayana talks about a woman returning a man's kiss, making it clear that a woman can also initiate the kiss. This can also apply to other forms of lovemaking. So, women shouldn't feel afraid to make the first move.

To perform this kiss, as you kiss your lover's upper lips, she returns the kiss by kissing his lower lip. You can increase the sensuality of the kiss by kissing your partner's upper and lower lips in turn. And like most kisses, you and your lover can have it sitting, standing or lying down.

The Clasping Kiss

This type of kiss is the one where either the woman or man takes both the lips of the other between her or his lips. However, for the woman, you can only enjoy taking this kiss when your lover doesn't have a mustache. That way, you don't have to get all those hair in your mouth.

When you are enjoying this type of kiss with your lover and your lover uses his/her tongue to touch the tongue, teeth, or palate of your lover, it's called the fighting of the tongue. Generally, in clasping kiss, scrupulous oral hygiene is important.

A Young Girl's Kiss

The young girl's kiss is a type of kiss the Kama text recommend for lovers who are about to have sex for the first time. There are different types of young girl's kiss, and it's recommended that the kiss is done moderately and not to be continued for a long time.

The nominal kiss: to have this kiss like a girl, use your mouth to touch your love's own. But don't do the touching yourself, approach your lover closely, and he would do the touching himself. *The throbbing kiss*: to have this kiss as a girl set your bashfulness aside touches the lips of her lover that is pressed into her mouth and with an object moves her lower lips but not the upper one.

The touching kiss: to have this kiss as the girl kiss your lover by using your tongue to touch his lips. As you close your eyes, place your hands on your lover's hands and enjoy the kiss.

Other ways to use kissing

Apart from the above-mentioned types of kissing, there are other ways you and your lover can engage in kissing. These different forms of kissing can be used for different purposes. Here are some examples of the different ways to use kissing.

Kissing that kindles love

Just like the name suggests, this kissing a woman can use to arouse her partner. She can use it to wake her partner up when she is feeling amorous. When she kisses him, she should look at his face while he sleeps. And she should kiss him passionately, softly and with desire. This type of kissing shows her intention and desires to her lover.

Kissing that awakens

In this type of kissing, lovers can quickly use it to rekindle the love they have for each other. A man can use this kissing on his lover. When a man comes home late in the night, for example, and he finds his lover asleep, he can then go to her and place a kiss on her. This kiss shows her his intention, and occasionally, the woman could even pretend to be asleep to wait for her lover to come home and kiss her this way.

Kissing that turns away

Now when your lover seems to be carried away, or his mind seems to be somewhere else, as a woman, you can use a kiss to turn his mind away. Perhaps you both just had a quarrel, or maybe he is attending a business or looking at something else, a kiss is perfect to bring his mind back to you.

Kissing the body

The lips and breasts are very sensitive parts of the body, and when touched with the mouth can bring lots of pleasure. In general. The closer you kiss your lover to the genitals, the more irresistible and intense the pleasure would be. The body should be kissed by both loves at the same time for more pleasure, especially around the foot to the head. The intensity at which you kiss the body should vary in terms of intense, moderate, pressed, or soft.

Breast kissing: when you want to kiss your lover's breast, be sure to apply it lightly to the fullness of the breast, as you gently suck and rub the nipples. You should pay special attention to the nipples because for many women; the nipple is a very powerful arousing point.

Kissing and licking: as lovers, you both should participate in kissing and licking. You should also pay special attention to areas like the inside thigh, the back of the knees, nipples, and breast. The greater you have self-control in delaying penetration, the richer the rewards when it finally occurs. You also combine the kissing and licking with a series of soft sensual strokes and kisses to enhance the effects of the kisses.

Biting

Loves can also engage in biting as a form of mouth play. Kama Sutra encourages it as it is an important part of the lover's repertoire. Biting can be done anywhere on the body and can range from playful nip to a more teasing than erotic, or it could be a sustained sucking that leaves a mark. Here are more details about biting you need to know as loves.

The biting of a boar

Lovers can use the biting of a boar when they want to leave a bite mark on their lover's shoulder. This bite is described as consisting of many board rows of marks near one another. It also usually have red intervals. You can make these markings on the shoulders as well as on the breasts which shows peculiar intense passion lovers have for themselves.

The broken cloud

This type of biting is described as consisting of unequal risings in a circle. This unequal circle is as a result of the space between the teeth. These type of biting is even best when you make a mark on the breast.

In addition to these two types of biting, there are eight other types of biting loves can engage in to show passion. These biting include the hidden bite, the swollen bite, and the point, the line of point, the coral and the jewel and the line of jewel.

Cunnilingus

Cunnilingus or oral sex where the virginal is being stimulated, and it is widely practiced in the modern world today. You should not run into trouble having this with your partner. Well, in some cases some partners feel somewhat irritated by the whole idea at first, but don't worry, you can talk them out of their irritation. And when you are able to talk them out of it, you can enjoy the sensation and special feeling of intimacy provided by oral sex.

Clitoral stimulation

Clitoral stimulation is a type of cunnilingus where the clitoris is gently stimulated with the lips or tongue. The clitoris is probably the most sensitive part of the woman's body, and as such, the clitoral stimulation would be exceedingly sensual. For this move, position yourself in a way that you can stroke your tongue over the shaft and head of her clitoris. If you like, your partner could be lying on her back, sitting or standing.

And if she's one of the many women that enjoy cunnilingus, she could experience a series or orgasm during the session. Stimulate the sides of the clitoris, run and you can go underneath too. Also, use your tongue to give feather-light strokes on the head of the clitoris and give it a flick underside of the shaft from the sides with the tip of your tongue.

Stimulating the perineum

To do this, let the woman open her legs widely, then you can get between them as you lick the perineum. The perineum is the area that lies between the vagina and the anus. This area is usually very rich in never endings and as such is very sensitive to touch. So use your tongue to touch, stroke and lick. When you stimulate the perineum properly, it can cause high arousal.

Fellatio

Unlike cunnilingus, that deals more of oral sex and mouth play on the virginal, fellatio is for male. It can be seen as mouth congress when the penis is stimulated until orgasm is experienced in most cases.

Licking the Penis

As a woman to start fellatio with your lover, start with licking his penis as though it were an ice cream cone. Then you can go ahead to hold the base of the penis with one hand and then use the blade of your tongue to lick the penis upward repeatedly. You can do this on one side and then on the other for maximum satisfaction.

Butterfly flick

The butterfly flick is another highly effective fellatio technique whereby you consistently flicker your tongue lightly on the ridge of the underside of your lover's penis. When you first start, you may need to hold the penis of your lover, but you would adapt to it in no time, and you would be able to perform it without having to use your hands. When you leave them as you caress and fondle the penis, pleases your lover even more.

CHAPTER 6:
KAMA SUTRA SEX POSITIONS EXPLANIED

I'm pretty sure this is the chapter you have long been waiting for, and as such I'd try my best to be as realistic with you as the positions can be. There are about a hundred sex positions explained in the Kama Sutra. But if I am to give you the full details of it, it would be somewhat too much for the budget of this book. However, who knows, I might write another book explaining only the sex position.

In that light, I would be explaining ten of the best sex position you and your partner can quickly try out to get the best sensual experience you've had in a while. So, without further ado, let's jump right into it.

1. The Pressing Position

The pressing position is one of the best and fulfilling positions you can try with your lover as it unfolds effortlessly from one embrace to a rhythm like lovemaking. This lovemaking is very sensual and can be used to connect with your partner deeply. And it is very easy to perform, and the best part is that both lovers would get to enjoy the lovemaking to the fullest.

To perform this lovemaking, lie your partner down on the bed after you must have had a series of foreplay. As she lies down on the bed, you can further go deeper with the foreplay by rubbing her breast, and nipples to arouse her further. Then you could go lower and play around her belly, and you approach her vagina. You could also place a kiss on

166

her vagina, and a little clitoris stimulation would also help as you go into position for this lovemaking. Remember your lover is already lying flat on the bed back down.

Then spread both of her legs on either side of your waist and fix yourself in- between. Then move a bit forward and place your hands at her sides and lean softly on her. Then at this position, you can go for insertion. Upon entering her vagina, go easy, it would feel a bit tight at first, but after a couple of minutes, and with the right amount of vagina fluid from arousing her well, things should go a lot more smooth. The main should use his feet to apply pressure when making love in this position.

The woman could also grip her partner's thigh with her own and press it inwards to tighten her vagina to thrust his penis more thigh for more friction and pleasure which increases the sensation for both of you. Generally, this position is great because of the body contact around the limb, and belly region as well. Moreover, the more the partners roll around together as they press their limb together, the greater the sexual charge would be.

2. The Mare's Position

This is also another sex position from the Kama Sutra worth taking a look at as lovers. One of the advantages of this technique is that it can be done in various positions. And if the woman is those that contract during orgasm, then she could employ her vaginal muscles to squeeze her lover's penis as though she were milking the penis. This sex position is highly pleasurable, that is why I'm featuring it in this book.

To actually enjoy this position, as the man you can enjoy it in two positions – either lying back down. Or sitting with one hand on the bed for support. As usually, sex should always proceed after a series of foreplay. When emotions are high, and the two of you are really in the mood and want to dive into each other, then man should go to bed. As I said earlier, you can either take a seated position of back down position.

In that position, the woman crosses her legs over yours and faces the same direction you are facing. So, her back would be at your front. In that position, before you go for congress, you can further to do a little more foreplay, like kissing her back, playing with her hair, or squeezing the breast would not be a bad idea.

Then you can go for penetration as the man. On entering the vagina with your penis, it is best you take the lying down position at first as it helps reveals more of the penis for deeper penetration. As you penetrate, you can then sit up for more joyride. After some time enjoying this position with your partner, you feel very close to orgasm, you could take the sitting position as it helps to reduce the feeling of orgasm. You could also help by stimulating her clitoris with your fingertips as you sit up. She could also do this herself, whichever you two lovebirds prefer would be just fine. One thing you both will enjoy again in this position is the skin contact because it is more like she is sitting on your lap. This sense alone can increase arousal to make the man have an orgasm in no time. Because you'd both feel the buttock bouncing on the laps making those clapping sounds turning both lovers on more. This position is enjoyable, and lovers should try it out.

3. The Turning Position

When couples are making love, alternating the position can help to make lovemaking more intense and sensual as well as increase closeness. The turning position is a perfect type of love, making that is perfect for this kind of feeling. To have the turning position lovemaking with your lover, have a couple of foreplay to make the woman end up with her back on the bed. Then as the man fix yourself in-between her legs and go for the insertion.

The lovemaking is more like the popular missionary lovemaking, but it comes with a twist. During lovemaking, the man can change position by lifting one of his legs and turn around without withdrawing from her. There are different ways the man can turn around in this position. There are about four different stages in this turning position.

The first stage is just like what I just explained above, the regular missionary position. The woman can caress and stroke the chest of her lover to give him more arousal, which can be a tricky maneuver. For the second stage, the man would lift his left leg and then his right leg to his lover's right leg and should not withdraw his penis from her vaginal.

The third stage involves the man moving both of his legs around, and this time, he does it without withdrawing his penis. He should make sure his body is at the right angle with his lover. Her legs also should be slightly apart as it would make it easier for him to keep his penis inside her vagina. And for the woman, she should lie back and enjoy the unusual angle of penetration. And the last fourth position is when he makes a complete 180-degree rotation in the sense that his body is between her legs one leg on either side of her shoulders. Navigating through these four stages of sex position is a bit difficult. But with practice, you would become a master in it in no time.

4. The Woman on Top Position

The woman on top is just like the turning position mentioned above, but this time around, the woman is on top of the man in this position. Again it comes in three different stages which the woman can use to vary the position while making love to make lovemaking more fun. To have this form of lovemaking with your partner, the man should lie back down.

The woman would then cross her legs one on either side of the man. As she sits on her lover, they should both lock their fingers together. Then as she balances herself on her partner's lap, the congress should happen. While making love in this position, then you both should switch positions. The first stage is when the woman is in the normal facing her lover while they make love.

The second stage is when she tilts both of her legs to her lovers left side or right side depending on whichever side she prefers. She could keep her legs together for more sensual feeling as her vaginal would be tight. Or she could spread her legs to make the vaginal a little bit more open. She can then steady herself by putting a hand on his knee and the other hand on his chest for support.

The third and last stage is when the woman makes a full complete rotation where she now backs the man. She can place her hand on her lover's leg as she rides him. She could make movements like she's tweaking on his penis to make the sex faster and more sensual.

5. The Yawning Position

The yawning position is somewhat popular, but not everyone gets it right. This lovemaking position starts with a man in a more-or-less kneeling position. However, his knees should be widely spread. Not too wide, though! It should just be the right width for the woman to fit. Then the woman lying with her back on the bed raises her thigh and parts them on either side of the man. Her legs might get tired with time, so she can press her legs against his side to make it easier to keep them up.

This position is pleasurable for both the man and the woman, but for the woman, it's all about getting the right thigh angle. Now, since the woman is lying down back on the bed, and the man on top (kneeling), pressing her thighs together, his side is an easy way to vary her thigh angle. Adjusting her thigh angle is also a way of varying the depth of penetration. Also, the barrier of the woman's thigh doesn't allow very deep penetration, but her clitoris gets much stimulation.

The man, on the other hand, should thrust himself forward gently against the woman's lower thigh for the penetration. He should also interlace his hands with the woman's hand to keep him up while penetrating. In general, this position is really erotic. Not to mention, her genitals are exposed, which turns the man on more. The helplessness she feels being on the bed in that locked position can also be a powerful turn on for both of them.

What you should note about this position is that her leg would feel a bit heavy with time since blood wouldn't flow much to her legs. So, don't use this position for a prolonged period. Also, since the man is somewhat resting on her hands, her hand would also feel tired at some point. Plus if you're a fan of fast sex, this position wouldn't really work for you. This position is for people who prefer a more gentle to a moderate speed of sex.

6. The Elephant Posture

This sex position is highly recommended as it is very sensual and comes with a lot of joy attached. This position is so powerful because there are lots of body contact involved in the position. Lovers who want to connect with each other deeply can have a fun time enjoying this position. To perform this position, very little is needed to know about from the right foreplay that would lead to this position.

To begin lovemaking in this position, start with the right foreplay that would make you get to your lovers back. Kissing her whole body round could be a great start. Or you can combine kissing her body with a little hair play and then find your way to her back. Kiss her shoulder and bend her over until she's lying down with her stomach, thigh, breast, and feet all touching the bed. In this position, you could go for a little massaging to stimulate her even more.

Massage her back, and go down a little to massage her buttocks. Massage her around her vagina and stimulate her clitoris until she fills wet on her vagina. Then you can go for the penetration, for the penetration, place your hands and either side of your lover and lean on her buttock a bit. Then like you, as you go for the penetration, pass your penis between her slightly parted legs and get into her vagina.

This sex position is very sensual as you would enjoy the feeling of her buttock around the penis, which is very pleasurable. The woman can intensify the sensation for both of you by pressing her thigh closely once the man is insider her to increase the feeling.

7. Level Feet Posture

This position is a type of Ananga Ranga way of lovemaking. This position can be a bit difficult to do and is not a position that can be enjoyed for a prolonged period of time. To perform this lovemaking, you need to find a way to end the foreplay with the woman back on the bed. But if you are a couple who love to have deep penetration, sex would definitely enjoy this type of lovemaking as the position reveals the vagina in a way that penetration can go deep.

To perform this lovemaking, with the woman is lying down, raise her legs up and place them on your shoulder. One leg on either side of her partner as she pushes herself closer towards his penis. Then the man supports her by holding her sides around her rib and then goes for the penetration. As he goes for the penetration, she could increase the pressure by closing her thing, which would make the penetration more pleasurable on his deep-plunging penis.

8. The Crab Embrace Position

As lovers, if you want a sex position that you can do for a very prolonged period, then this is perfect for you. The crab and embrace position is more of a side-by- side position in the sense that you and your partner are both lying down side by side facing each other. The penetration in this position would be deep. However, the man's movement would be restricted in a way. This sex position is very sensual as you can look deep into your lover's eyes as you make love and use your hands to caress each other. You both could even have a deep sensual kiss in-between the sex.

To perform this inviting and warm sex position, the man would lie right next to the woman and places one of his legs in-between her legs. In this lying position, he then goes for the penetration. And like I said earlier, the penetration movement wouldn't be much, so done expect too much movement. This position is also great, especially when you and your lover have been having sex for a prolonged time, and you are both tired but still passionate to have sex.

When the sex is going on in this position, you can add loving caresses to the mix. Use your free hand to caress each other's face, torso, arms, thighs, and buttocks. Again, the leg position is also important in this sex position, so make sure you put your uppermost leg over his body and rest your knee back to his hip.

9. The Rainbow Arch Position

It is never a bad idea to try something new, and this sex position is definitely going to be something new in your archive. This sex position is somewhat difficult, but when you get a hold of the idea of the position, it will come in a lot easier. This sex position is a side by side sec position, and the posture has an unusual angle for penetration, which has a very sensational feeling attached.

To perform this sex position with your lover, you and your lover are to both lies down flat on the bed. As the woman lies down, she is to raise one of her legs up sure that the man can fix himself in-between her opened legs. The man should fix himself, in-between her legs in such a way that his face goes to the back of the woman while his legs come to her front. Then as he goes for the penetration, he holds her shoulder to make the movement easier. She can hold his leg for support, so she doesn't move too much while the man applies more pressure for the lovemaking.

10. Driving the Peg Home

This is a standing posture sex position. It might involve some strength from the man's side, but it is definitely worth the strength. Strength is needed in the sense that the man would need to lift the woman up for the penetration. So, for lovers to enjoy this sex position, the man needs to be strong so that he can thrust his penis satisfactorily while bearing the weight of his partner. However, great care is needed because his member is very vulnerable to damage in this position so he should take great care when making love with this position.

To perform this position. The man should lift the woman and support her up by holding her buttocks. Then she is to thrust her legs at either side of her lover but to hold on to her lover's waist tightly while she holds his shoulder. She is also to keep her back straight as she leans against the wall.

CHAPTER 7:
BEFORE AND AFTER SEX

Now that you have all you need to know about the Kama Sutra, it is now that time where we are to talk about what is to be done before and after sex. Well, in summary, you should do those things that increase your passion before sex and those things that keep the amusement after sex. If you are having sex with your partner, there should be something that should be done before and after depending on your relationship with your lover.

The things you are to do varies, for example, if you don't want to risk having a baby after the sex, or you're scared of sexually transmitted diseases, which is very common in this modern world. So, in order to avoid stories that touch, it is in everyone's interest that lovers take the necessary precautions.

What to do before sex by having a safer sex

When having sex, it is very important that you bring the risk involved to the minimum. If you completely trust your partner, then there is no need for this safer sex. But if on the other hand, you just got a new partner and you're considering having sex, it is the only saver to protect yourself. Or at least it is important you have protected sex unite you are sure your lover is clear. Probably when you both have gone for a checkup, or a test, only then can you fully relax your mind of the safety of your partner.

There are two ways I am going to be talking about in which players can indulge in for safer sex. These two safer sex methods include non-penetrative sex and the use of condoms. Let us look into these two a bit to see what we can learn from them regarding safety before sex.

Non-Penetrative Sex

This is a type or method of having sex which is very sensitive to the lovers, but there is no penetration involved. Non-penetrative sex could include applying dry kissing, stroking, massage and embracing or a combination of any one of them. When you do not want to lose the closeness you have with your partner yet you do not want to risk any sexually transmitted infection, then you can both indulge in non-penetrative sex.

Mutual masturbation can also be a great way of having non-penetrative sex. But to be extra safe, make sure no vaginal fluid or semen comes in contact with your hands in case of any cuts, open sores, or abrasion on your hand.

Using Condoms

Using a condom is one of the safest ways to have sex without having to go through all the trouble of worrying too much. The major objective of using a condom is to interrupt your body and your lover's body fluid like semen or vaginal fluid from coming in contact during sex. Again condoms could also reduce the sensation a man feels his penis during lovemaking.

To use a condom, carefully remove it from the packet and squeeze out the air in the condom. Then hold the tip of the forefinger and thumb and with slow sensuous movement slide the condom down your partner's penis. And if your partner is not circumcised, gently push the foreskin back before unrolling the condom on his penis.

What to do after sex by prolonging the mood

After lovemaking, you and your partner could still keep the vibes going by engaging yourself to one or more activities that would keep the mood up. A lot of couples have confirmed that after having sex, they find it easier to communicate with each other. Some couples find it easier to talk about things while having sex, and others prefer having a conversation after having sex. In a case where you don't intend to continue having sex, but the man had, and orgasm but the woman didn't get the opportunity to reach climax, the ideal thing for the man to do is to masturbate her until she reaches orgasm.

Rekindle the excitement

Rekindling the excitement is a way lovers could spark up the mood to continue having sex. For example, a woman can renew the erection of her lover by gently fondling his testicles. She could use one hand to slide the other up and down his penis. Another scenario is enhancing the arousal of the man's penis. To further enhance the arousal, she could brush the head of his penis by making featherlight circular strokes with her hand.

As a man, you can rekindle the excitement by helping your lover get to orgasm. This is exceedingly important in a case where your partner was not able to reach a climax during lovemaking. Or a man could do this for his lover if she wants more orgasm, but you are not ready for more love again. You can help her by using your fingers to stimulate the clitoris. Gently run the tip of your finger along the underside and each side and on top of her vagina as you stimulate.

Sustaining the harmony

A lot of lovers don't want to give up the warm glow they get from making love by going to sleep of turning over, or by doing anything that is intellectually, or physically demanding. Some loves love to follow lovemaking with a gentle sensual massage, while others prefer to lie down quietly in each other's arms. In all, there can sustain harmony by engaging in other things. Things like eating together or any other undemanding activity would work just fine.

CHAPTER 8:
THE BENEFITS OF KAMA SUTRA

Kama Sutra is a very wonderful text that teaches us a lot about sex. As lovers, it is important that you take the teachings of Kama Sutra seriously so that you would be able to create a more stable relationship. As you already know, the Kama Sutra goes far deeper than talking about sex. Although the book talks about sex positions, the book also makes emphasis on ways of having a satisfying sex life. Following the Kama Sutra teachings, you stand a chance to become more educated about male and female. Here is some truth about the Kama Sutra you probably didn't know.

1. Kama Sutra values empowering women

Despite all what our modern-day society keeps preaching about women and sexuality, Kama Sutra has a different view on this subject matter. Kama Sutra suggests that a woman needs to study the different forms of sex before she gets married. When a woman understands the different forms of sex, she would be a better mate and would be more desirable by her man. So, the Kama Sutra encouraging women and empowering them is one of the biggest benefits you stand to gain from the book.

2. Kama Sutra makes a clear classification of a man's penis

Also, the Kama Sutra made mention of the size of a man's penis and that it matters when choosing a mate. There are three types of man penis by Kama Sutra – the bull, horse, and hare. Kama Sutra also made mention of different sizes of woman's vagina, and that a perfect match of the vagina size and penis sizes would result in a good sexual experience. In a case where you are married to a woman where the man's penis size and the woman's vaginal size is not a perfect match, then such couple would experience a little setback in the different sexual positions they can try out. So, thanks to Kama Sutra, we can make the right choice regarding the penis and vaginal sizes to enjoy a full sensual experience.

3. Kama Sutra also emphasizes on living a healthy life and well-balanced one

Kama Sutra is also a book that talks about tips on how to live a healthy life. The Kama Sutra encourages that a man and a woman should embrace cleanliness which would, in turn, boost their health. A man, for instance, should shave his beard on a regular basis, and take his bath and eat healthily, and the same applies to a woman too. She should bread her hair and shave as well. Couples could also try mutual grooming.

4. Kama Sutra talks about enticing and approaching women

The Kama Sutra also talks about interesting tips a man can use to entice and approaching a woman. This tip helps men to know how to touch and caress a woman in other to express their desire when they want to have sex. When a man knows these various tips and how to use them, he will find it easier to get his message over to the woman. The tips of how to entice and approach a woman further move on to touching and embracing.

5. Kama Sutra talks about eight different types of embrace

There are different types of embrace from the Kama Sutra. It further tells us that there are up to eight different types of embrace which can be used for different purposes. Because of Kama Sutra teaching, we now know how to apply the various types of embrace. And on applying the right type of embrace at the right moment would set the right mood in motion. So, rather than keeping all your emotions inside, you can now use the various teaching from Kama Sutra about embrace to seduce and lure your lover into that perfect love zone.

6. Kama Sutra teaches about kissing

There are different forms of kissing too. Kama Sutra also teaches that a woman should feel too shy about a kiss. We all know that a man in most cases is the ones that initiate the kiss, but a woman should not feel shy to be the one to start the kiss first. There are also different types of kiss that partner can use to deeply connect with each other at particular points in your relationship. Like a type of kissing couples can engage in when walking on a lonely street. There are also different types of kiss that lovers can engage in when they want to make love.

7. Kama Sutra is divided into a set of 64 acts

Contrary to the belief that the Kama Sutra doesn't have a list of sex position howbeit lovemaking that includes penetration is divided into 64 acts. This acts explains the different ways couples can have sex to enjoy the maximum pleasure from sex. To have the best sex, you have to combine it with stimulating desire, and engaging in an embrace, caressing, kissing, biting, slapping, moans, oral sex, and everything in-between.

8. Kama Sutra recommends that your scratch your partner

There are different types of scratch you can have with your partner. With this knowledge Kama Sutra provide us, we can add a twist to lovemaking without loved ones. Moreover, leaving scratch marks on your lover's body can help keep the fire burning for each other even when your lover is not close to you.

9. Kama Sutra recommends that your woman lover should reach orgasm first

When making love with our loved once, Kama Sutra suggests that the woman should be the first to have an orgasm. This point is valid because of the extreme exhaustion a man feels after having an orgasm, whereby he wouldn't be able to proceed with sex at least not immediately. So, in other to have great sex, the woman should be the first to have an orgasm before the man allows himself to have an orgasm.

10. Kama Sutra also talks about a woman's sex as being more than just sex penetrations

In Kama Sutra, there is more to sex than penetration for a woman. To a woman, the whole act is sensual, but to a man reaches orgasm at the end of the intercourse. Most men think that making a woman have an orgasm is their ultimate act, but a woman needs both sexual and physiological pleasure to be able to satisfy her urge. Thanks to Kama Sutra, many men who were getting this concept wrong have been able to make adjustments.

CHAPTER 9:
HOW TO APPLY EVERYTHING YOU'VE LEARNT ABOUT KAMA SUTRA

Now that you have completed reading this book, you may wonder what is next? Well, what happens next is to apply all you've learned from the Kama Sutra. There is no point in learning something like the Kama Sutra without applying it. What was given in this book are all practicable most of which are information gotten from friends and families, personal experience, and from various researches? So, feel completely free to try out any sex position that caught your attention.

When you can successfully apply everything you have learned about Kama Sutra from this book, you would experience a bit change in your sexual life. Now, if you are feeling a bit confused on how to apply Kama Sutra, don't worry I've got you covered. I've put together five easy to learn a step-by-step process you can follow to apply Kama Sutra to your love life successfully.

1. Approach your lover

The first and most important thing you need to do is first to make an approach. If you do not make a harmless approach, you would never know what your partner loves, and what they don't. There are different ways you can approach your lover about the whole idea of the Kama Sutra. Many people often prefer to just come out clean with the whole idea of the Kama Sutra, which normally works for them. They often come back with a smile on their face that by simply talking with their partner was all they needed.

However, it isn't everyone that is endowed with this gift. So, if you know deep down your lover would have second thoughts about the Kama Sutra, don't bother approaching her with a conversation of the Kama Sutra, rather show it to her. Make her feel a difference in you, more like a new you.

2. Make an Attempt

Next step you are to take after deciding what approach you want to use to lure your partner into Kama Sutra, is to make an attempt. Now, this step is very crucial as you wouldn't want to rush things a little too much. So, start with the basics. Don't attempt with her with difficult sex positions; in fact, try to avoid the sex positions when you start. Keep your attempts to foreplay and kissing.

You don't want to speak your lover or make them feel disgusted by the Kama Sutra because they are not used to it. And you know what they say about the first impression, it last longer. So, make sure you give your lover a really memorable first impression. Make her feel those sensations, touch her at those sensitive points we talked about the erogenous zones. Play around with her, make her laugh, make her feel something so sensual that she'd have to close her eyes and open her mouth because she can't hold it in altogether.

3. Seduce

When you're making the right attempt, and it seems to be working, that is just perfect because what you're going to do next is to go for the seduction part. This could be the part where you add a little massage to the mix. Try massaging her with oil, or better still dry but make it a full naked both massage. Then as you massage her, occasionally go towards her buttocks, go towards her vaginal area, and stimulate the clitoris from time to time. And don't forget also to rub and massage the breast as well.

For the man, be sure to massage his penis and around his balls, a blow job too would go a long way in causing arousal. Seduction should be very sensual and filled with so much emotion. If you want to do it right, make sure the environment is conducive. We've spoken about making the environment perfect, so be sure to employ it the right way. Make the room warm when it is cold outside, or cold wand well aerated when it is warm outside.

4. Go for any of the sex positions you've learned

When you have finally groomed your lover to the extent that all they can think about is sex with you, then you're halfway there. At this point, this is when you are going to apply the best sex position you've learned. Also, don't start with something too difficult. Go for something very simple, something very pleasurable, and something that is more of pleasure than of a sex position itself.

As soon as you go for in penetration, be sure to take things slowly at first. Don't also forget to stimulate other parts of her body as you continue to make love to her. Then feel free to change sex position from time to time as you progress in love.

5. Try an after sex fun

Last but not least, after sex, you can engage in a conversation with your lover. Ask him or her what they like about sex, so you can know where to shift and make an adjustment. With time, you'd only get better and making romantic hot crazy sex with your lover.

CONCLUSION

The world waits for no man. When you have a plan for your life, especially a life- changing program, do not procrastinate. There are more things you stand a chance to win. So, no matter the challenge you face on the road, always keep pushing forward. You might try to attempt Kama Sutra, but your lover keeps turning the idea down over and over. In such a case, don't give up, things can get very challenging, but with perseverance, you will achieve great things.

"Go for it now. The future is promised to no one" – *Wayne Dyer*

REFERENCES

Askmen editors February 20 2019 Best sex positions to improve your sex life

https://www.askmen.com/dating/love_tip_250/274_love_tip.html

Nicole Blades july 11, 2019 This is what your sex position bucket list should look like

https://www.womenshealthmag.com/sex-and-love/a19943165/sex-positions-guide/

26 sex positions that'll get off every time

https://www.muscleandfitness.com/women/sex-tips/26-sex-positions- thatll-get-her-every-time

What is sex?

http://teenhealthsource.com/sex/introduction-sex/

Kenny Thapoung and Meagan Drillinger October 12 2018 19 crazy sex positions that have been missing from your life

https://www.womenshealthmag.com/sex-and-love/a19907142/crazy-sex-positions/

Celeste morales Why sex is important in a relationship

https://www.finehomesandliving.com/Why-Sex-is-Important-in-a-relationship/

Reviewed by A driana Rough sex :The intensely passionate in-depth guide

https://badgirlsbible.com/how-to-have-rough-sex

Punchng march 24 2017. 12 sex positions men are ready to die for

https://punchng.com/12-sex-positions-men-are-ready-to-die-for/

8 sultry sex positions to spice up your sex life

https://www.durexusa.com/blogs/explore-sex/8-sultry-sex-positions-to-spice-up-your-sex-life

Sean Jameson 119 best sex positions

https://badgirlsbible.com/best-sex-positions

CPSIA information can be obtained
at www.ICGtesting.com
Printed in the USA
BVHW030203200421
605382BV00006B/179